COOKBOOK FOR DIABETICS
AND ALL THE FAMILY

COOKBOOK
FOR
DIABETICS
AND ALL THE FAMILY

SECOND EDITION 1972
COMPLETELY REVISED
OVER 50 NEW RECIPES ADDED

BURNS & MacEACHERN LIMITED
Toronto   Canada

FIRST EDITION, 1963
REPRINTED
1964, 1966, 1967
1968, 1970, 1971
SECOND EDITION, 1972

ISBN 0-88768-028-3

Printed and bound in Canada

PREFACE

All of us who work in the field of carbohydrate metabolism have one great aim — to improve the lot of diabetics everywhere. I am honoured to be invited to write a Preface to this Cookbook for Diabetics which has been compiled by The Canadian Diabetic Association in collaboration with The Ontario Dietetic Association. It has been written with great care by a panel of experts and will prove of inestimable value to all who are interested in this disorder. We can be justly proud of the excellence of the material and clarity of presentation in this "all Canadian" Cookbook.

Charles H. Best.

Charles H. Best, C.C., C.H., C.B.E., M.D., F.R.S.
Honorary President
The Canadian Diabetic Association

v

ACKNOWLEDGEMENTS

The authors gratefully acknowledge the contributions made by:

Members of The Canadian Diabetic Association

Members of the Dietetic Associations in Newfoundland, Nova Scotia, Quebec, Ontario, Manitoba, Saskatchewan and Alberta

Information and Consumer Service, Department of the Environment, Ottawa

Food Advisory Services, Consumer Section, Canada Department of Agriculture

Dr. C. K. Gorman, Dr. Gordon D. Brown and other Members of the Clinical and Research (Scientific) Section, The Canadian Diabetic Association

Dr. A. M. Fisher, The Canadian Diabetic Association

A special word of thanks is extended to Mrs. A. E. Shields and her son James Shields, who prepared the final manuscript for the first edition in 1963.

FOREWORD

The diabetics of Canada have reason to know how helpful a dietitian can be. In every province, devoted professionals are spending much of their time and energy on activities related to the dietary management of this important group of people.

One of the most effective services provided by The Canadian Diabetic Association in recent years has been a consistent program of diet counselling. Through a gift from the Atkinson Charitable Foundation, and latterly from the Connaught Medical Research Laboratories, a qualified professional dietitian serves as National Diet Counsellor for The Canadian Diabetic Association. A grant from the Gladys and Merrill Muttart Foundation has enabled the establishment of Diet Counselling Service in Western Canada, with a qualified professional dietitian in charge.

Doctors and dietitians in every part of Canada have been encouraged to unify dietary practices in connection with diabetes. One of the most important factors in the successful development of this aim has been the production and publication of the Exchange Lists for Meal Planning for Diabetics in Canada. Produced in collaboration with a committee of professional dietitians representing every province in Canada, this valuable booklet has been revised four times since the original edition was published in 1956. A total of more than 500,000 copies are now in use by diabetics, dietitians, nurses and doctors across Canada.

Probably as a result of the widespread use of the Meal Planning Booklet, many requests were received by The Canadian Diabetic Association for recipes and menu ideas which would make the regular meals of a diabetic more interesting and palatable. These requests prompted The Canadian Diabetic Association to enlist again the help of dietitians. A special Committee of members of The Ontario Dietetic Association accepted the challenge. Their thought and effort and enthusiasm resulted in the First Edition of the Cookbook for Diabetics, published in 1963. Now, in 1972, some members of the original Committee have been joined by younger members of the profession to review and revise the Cookbook. We are certain that it will continue to serve a useful purpose, along with the Exchange Lists for Meal Planning for Diabetics in Canada.

Sometimes the question is asked, "Why do we need manuals, cookbooks and meal planning booklets specifically for Canada?" The answer is a simple one. Because of variations in available foods, traditional dishes and regional preferences, the eating habits of Canadians DO DIFFER from those in other countries...even the United States. But more important for diabetics is the fact that household measurements and standards for diet prescriptions also differ from one country to another, to the extent that errors in construction of a diabetic diet might be made if the wrong references were used.

I am confident that all those who have seen or benefited from the success in dietary treatment of diabetes join me in expressing sincere thanks to the dietitians who have contributed so much of their time and knowledge to this highly successful venture.

Harold H. Alexander

Harold H. Alexander
President,
The Canadian Diabetic Association

INTRODUCTION TO SECOND EDITION

Diabetics, this book is for you! Your meals CAN be flavourful and attractive, and still conform to your prescribed daily meal plan. The Cookbook for Diabetics has been compiled to help you and your family prepare and serve appetizing, nutritionally adequate meals and to provide new ideas and culinary inspiration to your daily meal planning. In this new edition we have even added a Gourmet Section!

To make this book possible, a special Committee was formed in 1959 by The Ontario Dietetic Association at the request of The Canadian Diabetic Association. This 1972 edition has been prepared by a similar Committee, reactivated by The Ontario Dietetic Association. In both cases, recipes were collected from dietitians and members of The Canada Diabetic Association. All recipes have been home-tested for palatability, appearance and ease of preparation. The final selection of recipes includes popular choices which will add variety to menus, give satisfaction and pleasure in eating, and fit the average family budget. Most recipes yield enough for an average family, so you, the diabetic, may share the same menu as other family members. The exchange value is given for one serving of each recipe, in terms of the Food Exchange Lists in the C.D.A. Meal Planning Booklet. Thus you can see at a glance how it will fit into your diabetic meal plan.

The following members of The Ontario Dietetic Association wish you success and enjoyment as you use this book:

ORIGINAL COOKBOOK COMMITTEE (1963)
Joan Benedict, R.P.Dt.
Edythe Card, R.P.Dt.
Ola Cikalo, R.P.Dt.
Barbara Hone, R.P.Dt.
Isabel Lockerbie, R.P.Dt.
Muriel Patterson, R.P.Dt.
Corinne Trerice, R.P.Dt.

REVISIONS COMMITTEE (1972)
Frances Berkoff, R.P.Dt.
Marthe Brouillette, R.P.Dt.
Ann Brown, R.P.Dt.
Dorothy Jones, R.P.Dt.
Linda Lanning, R.P.Dt.
Isabel Lockerbie, R.P.Dt.
Muriel Patterson, R.P.Dt.
Myra Smithies, R.P.Dt.
Corinne Trerice, R.P.Dt.

ix

CONTENTS

BETTER FOOD PREPARATION

Although food preparation for the diabetic is a serious and exacting responsibility, the diabetic should manage his diet . . . the diet should not manage him! Eating can be a pleasure if these suggestions are kept in mind:

READ THE RECIPE CAREFULLY. The best cooks read the entire recipe and assemble all ingredients and equipment before starting, so preparation can proceed quickly and smoothly.

USE STANDARD MEASURING UTENSILS. Avoid errors and guessing by using a standard eight ounce measuring cup and standard teaspoon and tablespoon. Coffee mugs, tea cups and dessert or soup spoons are NOT SUITABLE for measuring purposes. When measuring fractions, use standard individual measures of ¼, ⅓ and ½ cup, and ¼ and ½ teaspoon.

MEASURE ACCURATELY. Recipes have been tested using standard, **level measurements.** To assure success in using these recipes, be certain to make every measurement carefully. Fill the measure, then level it with the edge of a knife or spatula. Do not guess!

ABBREVIATIONS USED IN THIS BOOK:

c. — cup
tbsp. — tablespoon
tsp. — teaspoon
oz. — ounce(s)
fl. oz. — fluid ounce(s)
f.g. — few grains

c.c. — cubic centimetre(s)
gm. — gram
lb. — pound
qt. — quart
pkg. — package

1

CHECK EQUIVALENT MEASURES

1 tablespoon	= 3 teaspoons
1 cup	= 16 tablespoons
⅞ cup	= 1 cup, less 2 tablespoons
¾ cup	= 12 tablespoons
⅔ cup	= 10 tablespoons plus 1 teaspoon
½ cup	= 8 tablespoons
⅓ cup	= 5 tablespoons plus 1 teaspoon
¼ cup	= 4 tablespoons
⅛ cup	= 2 tablespoons
30 grams	= 1 ounce by weight
30 cubic centimetres	= 1 fluid ounce
1 teaspoon	= 5 cubic centimetres or 5 grams by weight
1 tablespoon	= 15 cubic centimetres or 15 grams by weight
1 cup	= 8 ounces or 240 grams or 240 cubic centimetres (fluid)
1 Imperial quart	= 5 cups of 8 ounces each (in common use in Canada)
1 U.S. quart	= 4 cups of 8 ounces each (check this when travelling in the U.S.A.)

REFER TO EXCHANGE LISTS OFTEN. Throughout this book you will find reference to the Exchange Lists in The C.D.A. Meal Planning Booklet. Keep it handy. The exchange value of one serving of each recipe is stated, so you may easily calculate it as part of the daily meal plan of the diabetic.

YOUR FAMILY CAN ENJOY THESE FOOD IDEAS TOO! The recipes included in this book are not reserved for diabetics only. Often only one family member is a diabetic and he or she wants to enjoy the same foods as the rest of the family. You will find these recipes suitable for everyone. If you live alone or your family is small, many of the recipes may be recalculated for one or two servings. Be sure to INCLUDE ALL INGREDIENTS in the original recipe even though the smaller amounts seem less important. In some cases slight adjustments in seasoning may be necesary, but these will not affect the food value or calorie value of each serving, and therefore will not affect the exchange values.

WE DO NOT ADVISE ANY CHANGES IN RECIPES IN THE CHAPTER ON DESSERTS OR THE CHAPTER ON CAKES, COOKIES AND QUICK BREADS. Altering amounts of some ingredients in recipes in these Chapters will affect the type of exchanges represented in the final recipe. Thus, the exchange value for one serving given in the Cookbook will not be correct, and may affect your total meal plan.

SWEETENERS:

(a) ARTIFICIAL: There are several artificial sweeteners, in liquid and tablet form, available for use in food preparation. None of these contains any calories, and if used carefully can make prepared dishes, fruits, etc. more palatable. Liquid artificial sweeteners are often used for cooking purposes, as they mix easily with other ingredients. If tablets are used, they will dissolve more quickly if crushed first in a spoon. To obtain the sweetening value of one teaspoon of sugar

use ⅛ teaspoon liquid artificial sweetener

or ¼-grain tablet.

One word of caution . . . if foods are oversweetened with artificial sweeteners, they often develop a bitter flavour. Use too little rather than too much! If saccharin is the artificial sweetener used, it should be added AFTER COOKING.

(b) SUGARS: The use of sugar (sucrose) in these recipes may seem a contradiction to previous teaching, and thus cause concern about the advisability of using products sweetened with it, or using it in food preparation. One reason for this concern is that a person with diabetes is instructed not to use sugar. Sometimes the diabetic interprets this to mean that he must follow a "sugar free" diet. There is really no such diet applicable to everyday living. Milk and fruits contain sugar in their natural forms. Breads, biscuits and cookies usually contain sugar as an ingredient. Breads and cereals also contain starch, a form of carbohydrate which is converted into sugar during digestion.

REMEMBER: If sugar is called for in a recipe, do not be too alarmed. It represents a small proportion of the recipe's total carbohydrate content and was included when the exchange value of that recipe was calculated. However, this does not mean that sugar may be sprinkled on your cereal or fruit, or added to your favourite beverage, or used in any other way, except as specified in these recipes.

IF YOUR DOCTOR PRESCRIBES OTHER DIET RESTRICTIONS . . . these will have to be considered as you plan your diet and choose the foods for your daily meal plan. **BE SURE TO CONSULT YOUR DOCTOR OR A DIETITIAN** for help with your meal planning, if you are unsure about any directions you have been given. The following suggestions may help you understand how to handle your added restrictions:

3

(Better Food Preparation Cont'd)

(a) TO RESTRICT SALT OR SODIUM: Omit salt from all recipes, and add no salt during food preparation or at mealtimes. Choose recipes without baking soda and without commercial baking powders. The following seasonings and herbs may be safely used to make foods more palatable. Experiment with amounts to suit your own and your family's tastes:

anise	garlic	parsley
basil	lemon juice	pepper
caraway	mace	pimento
chives	marjoram	rosemary
cloves	mint	saccharin
coriander	mustard (dry)	tarragon
curry	orange peel	thyme
dill	onion juice	
fennel	paprika	

(b) TO ALTER FAT CONTENT: Any changes you make should be done strictly as your doctor prescribes them. If necessary, you may make substitutions in the recipes by using skim milk in place of whole milk, and by replacing butter or lard with margarine or a vegetable oil. Teflon coated cookware will help prevent sticking during cooking or baking if you cannot use added fat for frying or 'greasing' your baking pans.

(c) DO NOT ASSUME THAT ALL FOODS LABELLED "DIETETIC" ARE FOR DIABETICS: Changes in Food and Drug Regulations covering labelling of foods for special dietary use are currently being made. Regulations for carbohydrate reduced, calorie reduced and low calorie foods are carefully being outlined, so new labels and information on packages should help you decide which foods you can fit into your meal plan. READ LABELS AND PACKAGE INFORMATION CAREFULLY. Consult your nearest Health Protection Branch, or a dietitian if you need further explanations.

RELISHES AND APPETIZERS

Most diabetics do not need anything to sharpen their appetites at mealtime. But they do enjoy a party as much as anyone. If you are planning to serve relishes and snacks to diabetics at your next party, here are some suggestions.

Low Calorie Nibblers

If eaten in reasonably small amounts, as served on a relish tray, the following vegetables make attractive snack foods for the diabetic. In such amounts these could be counted as Calorie Poor Foods List B: celery curls, hearts or small sticks; carrot sticks or curls; flowerlets of raw cauliflower; small green onions or scallions; radish roses or thin slices of white icicle radishes; small Italian or cherry tomatoes; cucumber spears or thin slices; green and red sweet pepper slices or rings; mushrooms.

Canapés and Hors D'Oeuvres

A number of attractive canapés and hors d'oeuvres may be fitted into the day's food allowance. Remember that crackers, bread or melba toast used to carry fillings must be counted as outlined in the Bread Exchange List.

The Following Are Good with Appetizers

Exchanges	No. of Biscuits	
1 Calorie Poor Food List B	5 thin pretzels 2″ long	
1 Bread Exchange for any one of ⟶	3 Stoned Wheat Thins	6 saltines
	2 MacVita Crispbreads	5 Triscuits
	4 graham wafers	
½ Bread Exchange and 1 Fat Exchange	8 large potato chips	
1 Bread Exchange and 1 Fat Exchange for any one of ⟶	7 Cheese Ritz Biscuits	7 Ritz Biscuits
	14 Vegetable Thins	10 Bacon Dippers
	12 Triangle Thins	10 Onion Thins

TANGY LIVER PASTE

Yield: 1½ cups

Exchange 1½ tbsps. for: ½ Meat Exchange
and 1 Calorie Poor Food List B

Ingredients: ½ lb. beef liver
2 tbsps. chili sauce
1 tbsp. prepared mustard
1 tbsp. mayonnaise
2 tbsps. water
1 small clove garlic (optional)
½ tsp. salt
½ tsp. rosemary

Method: 1. Cook liver in boiling salted water until tender.
2. Remove skin, fibre and tubes.
3. Grind in food chopper, using fine blade; add chili sauce, mustard, mayonnaise, water, garlic, salt and rosemary, and put through the chopper a second time.
4. Blend together until smooth.
5. Form into a mound and chill thoroughly.

CHEESE "APPLE"

Yield: 1 cup

Exchange 1 tsp. for: 1 Calorie Poor Food List B
or *1 tbsp. for:* 1 Fat Exchange

Ingredients: 8 oz. plain white cream cheese
1 tsp. finely chopped onion
2 tbsps. finely chopped red and green pepper
2 tbsps. milk
paprika

Method: 1. Let cream cheese stand at room temperature until workable.
2. Add onion, peppers and milk; blend thoroughly.
3. Roll into ball and then cover with paprika, sprinkled on sheet of waxed paper.
4. Green pepper slivers may be placed on top as "apple leaves".
5. If you prefer not to use paprika, you will have a "snow ball".

Note: To make bite-size cheese balls, allow ½ tbsp. of mixture for each. Roll each ball in paprika or chopped parsely, or leave white. Exchange two cheese balls of this size for: 1 Fat Exchange.

DILL DIP

Yield: ¾ cup (12 tablespoons)
Exchange 2 tbsps. for: I Fat Exchange
Ingredients: ¾ cup commercial sour cream
    ¼ tsp. dried dill weed
    ¼ tsp. garlic powder
    ¼ tsp. salt
Method: 1. Mix all ingredients together and stir well.
    2. Refrigerate until serving time.

HOT BEEF CANAPES

Yield: 20 canapés
Exchange 2 Canapés for: ½ Meat Exchange
    and ½ Bread Exchange
Ingredients: 5 slices white bread
    2 tbsps. butter or margarine
    ½ lb. lean minced beef
    1 tsp. grated onion
    1 tsp. Worcestershire sauce
    ½ tsp. salt
    2 tbsps. chili sauce
Method: 1. Toast bread on one side only.
    2. Cut each slice into 1½" rounds with cookie cutter.
    3. Lightly butter untoasted side of bread rounds.
    4. Combine and mix ground beef, onion, Worcestershire sauce and salt.
    5. Roll into marble-size meat balls (1½ tsps. per ball).
    6. Place one meat ball on each buttered side of bread rounds; make a dent in centre of each meat ball.
    7. Broil until meat is done and bread is toasted around edges.
    8. Spoon chili sauce into each dent; serve hot.

BACON AND MUSHROOM ROLLS

Yield: 12 rolls
Exchange 1 roll for: 1 Fat Exchange
    and 1 Calorie Free Food List A
Ingredients: 12 mushroom caps (canned)
    12 strips bacon
Method: 1. Roll bacon strip around mushroom.
    2. Skewer with cocktail picks or toothpicks.
    3. Broil until bacon is cooked.
    4. Drain off the fat and serve hot.

SOUPS

Throughout the ages soup has been one of the most universal of mankind's foods. Today a wide variety of soups is available to add zest and satisfaction to meals. All types of soups may be included in the day's meals for the diabetic, if they are carefully made and if their food values are calculated as indicated in each recipe. Clear soups may be served as an appetizer before dinner. Vegetable soups, with a clear stock base or with a cream sauce base, may serve as part of the main course for lunch or supper. Chowders, thick with fish or meat and vegetables, may be the main course for any meal. For the diabetic who is ill, and whose diet must be restricted to soft or liquid foods, soup can provide ample nourishment in a form that is easy to eat.

The base for many homemade soups is soup stock made from meat, fowl or vegetables. Basic soup stock is a thin, flavourful liquid to which other ingredients may be added to make a variety of soups. Stock soups may be thickened if a heartier soup is desired. If homemade stock is not available, canned consommé or bouillon, or bouillon cubes dissolved in boiling water, may be used in any recipe calling for basic soup stock.

UNFLAVOURED SOUP STOCK

Yield: 4 cups
Exchange 1 cup for: 1 Calorie Free Food List A
Ingredients: 2 lbs. meat and bone (beef, veal, chicken or mutton)
6 cups cold water
Method: 1. Wash and cut meat into small pieces.
2. Add bones and cold water; soak 1 hour.
3. Broil until bacon is cooked.
4. Strain through moistened cheesecloth; save meat if desired.
5. Chill until fat is set.
6. Remove fat and discard it.
7. Refrigerate.

FLAVOURED SOUP STOCK

Yield: 4 cups

Exchange 1 cup for: 1 Calorie Poor Food List B

Ingredients: 2 lbs. meat and bone
6 cups cold water
1 small onion, cut in quarters
½ cup raw carrots, cut in chunks
2 stalks celery, cut in pieces
4 whole cloves
6 pepper berries
1 bay leaf
1 sprig parsley
1 tsp. salt

Method: 1. Proceed as for unflavoured soup stock; at end of 2nd hour of simmering the meat and bones, add vegetables and seasoning.
2. Simmer 1½ hours and finish as for unflavoured soup stock.

Unthickened Stock Soups

VEGETABLE SOUP

Yield: 4 servings

Exchange 1 serving for: 1 Vegetable Exchange List 2A

Ingredients: 3 cups soup stock
¼ cup diced carrots
¼ cup chopped onion
¼ cup shredded cabbage
¼ cup green beans, cut in strips
1 tbsp. celery, finely chopped
2 tbsps. diced turnip
salt, pepper and other seasonings to taste

Method: 1. Add prepared vegetables to the soup stock.
2. Cook until vegetables are tender (about ½ hour).
3. Season to taste; serve hot.

Note: Any combination of vegetables may be used in this recipe, as long as their exchange value adds up to 1 Vegetable Exchange List 2A, or 2 Vegetable Exchanges List 2B. If you wish to cook the vegetables separately, use only 2 cups soup stock. Add stock to cooked vegetables, reheat and serve.

9

PASTA SOUP

Yield: 4 servings

Exchange 1 serving for: 1 Vegetable Exchange List 2A
and 1 Calorie Poor Food List B

Ingredients: 2 cups soup stock
½ cup canned tomatoes or tomato juice
1 tbsp. finely chopped onion
1 tbsp. finely chopped celery or green pepper
½ cup cooked, drained macaroni
or ⅓ cup cooked, drained noodles, spaghetti or rice
¼ tsp. Worcestershire sauce
seasoning to taste

Method: 1. Bring to a boil soup stock, canned tomatoes, chopped onion and celery.
2. Add cooked macaroni, or noodles, or spaghetti or rice.
3. Reheat; season to taste.
4. Serve hot.

ONION SOUP

Yield: 4 servings

Exchange 1 serving for: 1 Vegetable Exchange List 2A
and 1 Fat Exchange

Ingredients: 4 medium onions
4 tsps. butter or margarine
3 cups soup stock
½ tsp. salt
⅛ tsp. celery salt
f.g. pepper
1 tsp. Worcestershire sauce

Method: 1. Peel onions; cut into thin slices.
2. Melt butter or margarine; add onion slices and brown lightly.
3. Add soup stock and simmer until onions are tender.
4. Add seasonings and serve hot.

Note: Just before serving, ½ cup grated Parmesan cheese may be added, if desired. If this is done, reheat the soup just until the cheese melts. With cheese, the exchange value of the soup would be:
1 Vegetable Exchange List 2A
and 1 Fat Exchange
and ½ Meat Exchange

TOMATO STOCK SOUP

Yield: 4 servings

Exchange 1 serving for: 1 Calorie Poor Food List B
and 1 Vegetable Exchange List 2B

Ingredients: 2 cups flavoured soup stock
1 cup canned tomatoes or tomato juice
2 tbsps. sweet green pepper, chopped
2 tbsps. lean cooked ham, chopped
1 tsp. butter or margarine
2 drops artificial liquid sweetener

Method:
1. Combine soup stock and tomatoes and heat slowly.
2. Cook green pepper and ham lightly in butter or margarine.
3. Add green pepper and ham to stock mixture.
4. Add salt and simmer ½ hour.
5. Add artificial sweetener and additional seasonings.
6. Strain and serve hot.
7. Garnish with chopped parsley or chives.

TOMATO CONSOMME

Yield: 4 servings

Exchange 1 serving for: 1 Calorie Free Food List A

Ingredients: 1 tin consommé (10 oz.)
½ cup tomato juice
¾ cup water
pinch of basil

Method:
1. Mix all ingredients and heat to serving temperature.
2. Serve hot, garnished with chopped parsley or a thin swirl of sliced lemon.

JULIENNE SOUP

Yield: 4 servings

Exchange 1 serving for: 1 Vegetable Exchange List 2B
and 1 Calorie Poor Food List B

Ingredients: 2 cups flavoured soup stock
2 tbsps. cooked carrot, cut in strips
2 tbsps. cooked turnip, cut in strips
1 tbsp. cooked peas
1 tbsp. cooked green or yellow beans, cut in strips
seasonings to taste

Method:
1. Heat soup stock.
2. Add cooked vegetables and reheat.
3. Season to taste and serve hot.

Thickened Stock Soups
CREOLE SOUP

Yield: 6 servings
Exchange 1 serving for: 1 Vegetable Exchange List 2A
and 1 Fat Exchange
Ingredients: 2 tbsps. butter or margarine
1½ tbsps. chopped green pepper
1 tbsp. chopped onion
3 tbsps. flour
2 cups soup stock
1 cup canned tomatoes
⅔ tsp. salt
f.g. pepper
f.g. cayenne pepper
1 tbsp. horseradish
¼ tsp. vinegar
⅓ cup cooked macaroni, cut in rings
Method: 1. Cook green pepper and onion in butter or margarine for about 5 minutes.
2. Add flour slowly, blending thoroughly.
3. Add soup stock and canned tomatoes, stirring to blend thoroughly.
4. Heat, stirring constantly until fully thickened; simmer 15 minutes.
5. Press through a sieve; add seasonings and reheat.
6. Add horseradish, vinegar and macaroni rings; serve piping hot.

MULLIGATAWNY SOUP

Yield: 6 servings
Exchange 1 serving for: 1 Vegetable Exchange List 2A
and 1 Meat Exchange
and 1 Fat Exchange
Ingredients: 1½ tbsps. butter or margarine
¼ cup each of diced carrots, onion and celery
½ cup diced raw apple, pared
1 cup diced cooked chicken
2½ tbsps. flour
1 clove
¼ tsp. pepper berries
1 sprig parsley
½ tsp. curry powder
2½ cups soup stock
½ cup canned tomatoes
salt, pepper and f.g. cayenne pepper

12

Method: 1. Cook diced vegetables, apple and chicken in melted fat until lightly browned.
2. Add flour and seasonings and blend thoroughly.
3. Add soup stock and tomatoes and stir over heat until fully thickened; simmer 1 hour.
4. Remove chicken with a perforated spoon or sieve; then press mixture through a sieve.
5. Return chicken to mixture. If liquid has cooked down, make up to 3 cups liquid with boiling water.
6. Reheat and serve hot.

Note: If desired, 3 tbsps. cooked rice per serving may be added to the soup after cooking. The exchange value of one serving then becomes:

   2 Vegetable Exchanges List 2A
  or 1 Bread Exchange
   and 1 Meat Exchange
   and 1 Fat Exchange

Cream Soups

Many milk soups may be made from the same base. This usually consists of vegetable soup stock and pulp, with milk added. Because these soups are usually thickened to the consistency of heavy cream, they are called "Cream Soups". They should be served very hot, and as soon as they are made.

BASIC RECIPE FOR CREAM SOUPS

Yield: 4 servings
Exchange 1 serving for: 1 Vegetable Exchange List 2A or 2B, depending on vegetable or vegetables used
     and 1 Milk Exchange

Ingredients: 4 tsps. butter or margarine
   3 tbsps. flour
   ¾ tsp. salt
   ⅛ tsp. pepper
   1½ cups vegetable stock and pulp mixed
   1½ cups skim milk

Method: 1. Melt butter or margarine, preferably in the top of a double boiler.
2. Blend in flour and seasonings.
3. Add vegetable stock and pulp gradually, stirring until fully thickened; cook until there is no taste of raw starch.
4. Add milk, either hot or cold, and reheat, but do not boil.
5. Serve at once.

CREAM OF POTATO SOUP

Yield: 4 servings

Exchange 1 serving for: 1 Bread Exchange
and 1 Milk Exchange

Ingredients: 1 small onion, coarsely chopped
1½ cups water
1½ cups skim milk
⅔ cup mashed potato
4 tsps. butter or margarine
1½ tbsps. flour
1½ tsps. salt
⅛ tsp. pepper
f.g. cayenne pepper
1 tsp. chopped parsley or grated raw carrot

Method:
1. Cook chopped onion in the water until tender.
2. Add skim milk and reheat.
3. Add this mixture slowly to the mashed potato and blend until smooth.
4. Blend flour and seasonings with the melted butter or margarine.
5. Gradually add potato-milk mixture, stirring constantly until fully thickened; cook until there is no taste of raw starch.
6. If desired, the soup may be strained; reheat and serve at once with chopped parsley or grated carrot garnish.

Note: 1 or 2 tsps. of crushed dried celery leaves, added during cooking, is a tasty addition.

CREAM OF MUSHROOM SOUP

Yield: 4 servings

Exchange 1 serving for: 1 Milk Exchange
and 1 Calorie Free Food List A

Ingredients: ½ cup chopped, canned mushrooms (save liquid)
or ½ lb. fresh mushrooms, peeled and chopped
4 tsps. butter or margarine
3 tbsps. flour
1 cup liquid from canned mushrooms
or 1 cup water
¾ tsp. salt
⅛ tsp. pepper
1½ cups skim milk

Method: 1. Cook mushrooms for 5 minutes in butter or margarine.
2. Mix flour with some of the cold mushroom liquid or cold water, to make a thin paste.
3. Add the remainder of liquid or water to mushrooms.
4. Heat this mixture to boiling.
5. Stir in flour paste slowly, stirring constantly until fully thickened; cook until there is no taste of raw starch.
6. Add milk and seasonings; reheat, but do not boil.
7. Serve at once.

CREAM OF TOMATO SOUP

Yield: 4 servings

Exchange 1 serving for: 1 Vegetable Exchange List 2A
and 1 Milk Exchange
and 1 Fat Exchange

Ingredients: 2 cups canned tomatoes
⅛ tsp. baking soda
3 tbsps. flour
1 tsp. salt
⅛ tsp. pepper
4 tsps. butter or margarine
2 cups whole milk

Method: 1. Heat tomatoes; press through a sieve if desired; add baking soda.
2. Add hot water to make up to two cups (liquid plus pulp).
3. In a separate saucepan, melt butter or margarine; blend in flour until smooth.
4. Add milk and seasonings to flour and fat mixture, stirring constantly until fully thickened; cook until there is no taste of raw starch.
5. Gradually add the hot tomatoes to the hot milk sauce, stirring to blend and avoid curdling.
6. Reheat to serving temperature. DO NOT BOIL.
7. Serve at once.

Variations: 1. Add 1 tbsp. finely chopped onion to the tomatoes before heating.
2. Add ¼ bay leaf to tomatoes while heating; remove bay leaf before adding tomatoes to milk sauce.

Note: For best results when making any type of Cream of Tomato Soup, have tomatoes and milk or milk sauce as close to the same temperature as possible. Never allow the mixture to boil.

UKRAINIAN BORSCH

Yield: 8 servings

Exchange 1 serving for: 1 Vegetable Exchange List 2A
and 1 Fat Exchange

Ingredients: 2 cups raw beets, cut in thin lengthwise strips
¼ cup raw onion, finely diced
½ cup green beans, chopped
⅓ cup green peas
1 cup cabbage, shredded
1 tsp. green dill
1 tbsp. parsley
8 cups water
1 tbsp. vinegar (white)
1 tbsp. flour
½ cup commercial sour cream

Method:
1. Place prepared vegetables in large saucepan.
2. Add water; simmer until vegetables are tender (1 - 1½ hours).
3. Fifteen minutes before serving add vinegar.
4. Just before serving, blend flour and sour cream; add very slowly to soup.
5. Stir constantly; reheat borsch but **do not boil.**
6. Season to taste.
7. Serve immediately.

Note: To exchange 1 serving for: 1 Vegetable Exchange List 2A, omit sour cream and increase vinegar to 2 tbsps.

CANNED CONDENSED SOUPS

Canned condensed soups may be included in meals for diabetics, if the following exchange values are used:

Exchange: 3 level tbsps. of the soup as it comes from the tin, for
either: 1 Vegetable Exchange List 2A
or: ½ Bread Exchange

For variety, a mixture of two kinds of canned soups may be used. The following liquids may be used to dilute the soup to the desired consistency:
Water: Free.
Clear broth, consommé or bouillon: 1 Calorie Free Food List A.
Milk, skim or whole: Subtract from milk allowance for the meal.

ADDITIONAL SUGGESTIONS FOR SEASONING SOUPS

These may be used for almost any soup, without changing the exchange value of the soup. Use sparingly: whole allspice; ground ginger; thin slices of lemon or lime; chopped parsley; paprika; sesame seed.

For bouillon: celery leaves or celery seed.

For chicken soup: chopped dill; a pinch of marjoram; rosemary leaves.

For consommé: a few cloves; mace; nutmeg; savoury; tarragon.

For fish soups or chowders: basil; bay leaves; curry powder; marjoram; sage; savoury; tarragon; watercress.

For oyster stew: mace; nutmeg; thyme.

For vegetable soup: basil; bay leaf; sage; savoury; watercress.

For asparagus soup: chives; sage.

For celery soup: thyme.

For tomato soup: basil; bay leaf; celery leaves; celery seed; curry powder; sage; tarragon.

For soup stock: crushed bay leaf; garlic; ½ tsp. monosodium glutamate.

For tomato, pea or vegetable soup: 1½ tsps. herb vinegar.

For canned soups: ½ tsp. monosodium glutamate.

SOUP ACCOMPANIMENTS

Soup is often more enjoyable with a crisp "bread" accompaniment. Soda biscuits, crackers and melba toast may be served, but they must be calculated as Bread Exchanges. For example —
1 Bread Exchange is equivalent to:
4 rectangular slices or 8 round slices of commercially made melba toast; **or** one 6-inch piece of matzoh; **or** 1½ rusks; **or** six 2-inch soda biscuits; **or** six 6-inch bread sticks (thin).

VEGETABLES

Vegetables are an integral part of the diabetic's meal plan. They do not need to be dull, but can be served in an endless variety of interesting ways. The diabetic may eat the same vegetables as the rest of the family, unless salt or sodium must be restricted. In either instance, the diet will be clearly marked: Low Salt **or** Low Sodium (see page 4).

The vegetables used may be fresh, frozen or canned. The size of serving will depend on the type of vegetable used and the number of vegetable exchanges allowed at the meal.

Most vegetables may be served either raw or cooked. They may be used in salads, soups and casseroles. Even when served as the vegetable course of the meal they may be cooked in a number of different ways, thus adding infinite variety and interest to such staple fare as carrots, turnips and peas.

Serving Hints:

Asparagus — serve hot or cold; delicious in salads, either plain or jellied.

Beans, yellow or green — serve hot or cold.

Beets — cook and serve hot with a little vinegar or lemon juice; cook, dice and serve cold in salad; pickle and sweeten to taste with artificial liquid sweetener.

Beet Greens — cook and serve hot; garnish with a wedge of lemon.

Broccoli — cook until tender and serve hot; garnish with a wedge of lemon.

Cabbage — cook and serve hot; in combination with other vegetables in soups or in casserole dishes; serve raw in cold salads.

Carrots — add colour to any meal; cook alone or with other vegetables, in a stew, in a number of other meat dishes or in soups; serve raw as carrot sticks or carrot curls, or grated in salads.

Cauliflower — serve raw or cooked; when cooked, serve hot or cold.

18

Celery — a very versatile vegetable; raw stalks may be filled with cheese or other filling; chop and add raw to salads; dice and cook in casserole dishes and soups; boil or braise and serve hot.

Note: Celery leaves, dried and crumbled or celery seeds add a piquant flavour to many dishes; both are Calorie Free Foods.

Chard — cook and serve hot; garnish with a wedge of lemon.

Cucumbers — serve raw or cooked.

Dandelion Greens — serve hot as beet greens or raw in salads. They must be green and tender.

Endive — an interesting and tempting salad green. Wash carefully!

Green Peppers — serve raw in salads, or cooked in casserole dishes and soups; as a stuffed vegetable see page 28.

Mushrooms — serve raw or cooked. For soup see page 14.

Onions — use in small quantities for flavouring meats, casseroles and soups as a Calorie Poor Food; boil, bake, or braise and serve as vegetable course.

Peas — usually served hot; cooked and chilled, use in salads.

Sauerkraut — serve steaming hot with pork chops, pork hocks or wieners; serve cold, if desired.

Spinach — cook and serve hot; garnish with a wedge of lemon; use raw in salads.

Squash — Hubbard, Pepper or Crook-necked; bake, steam or boil.

Tomatoes — probably the most versatile and enjoyable of all vegetables; serve hot or cold as outlined in the recipes for vegetables, soups, casseroles and salads.

Tomato Juice — serve hot or cold.

Turnips — dice, cook, mash and season; if desired, add a drop or two of artificial liquid sweetener while mashing; to add colour and flavour as a garnish for salad plates, slice raw turnip very thin and place in cold water to curl.

Turnip Greens — cook and serve hot as the other greens.

The following vegetables have a high starch content. Although they may be used as a Vegetable Exchange List 2A in very small servings, they are usually considered Bread Exchanges:

Artichokes; Beans, navy or lima, canned or cooked; Beans and Peas, dried; Corn; Parsnips; Potatoes.

19

CREOLE GREEN BEANS

Yield: 4 servings

Exchange 1 serving for: 1 Vegetable Exchange List 2A
and 1 Fat Exchange

Ingredients: 4 strips side bacon
½ medium-sized cooking onion, chopped
2 tbsps. diced celery
2 cups cooked green beans, fresh or canned
2 cups canned tomatoes
salt and pepper to taste

Method: 1. Cut bacon into small pieces and fry until crisp.
2. Remove bacon from pan; drain part of the fat from the pan; add the chopped onion and celery to the remaining fat and cook until golden brown.
3. Drain the fat from the onions and celery.
4. Mix the celery and onions with the beans, bacon and tomatoes in a baking dish.
5. Season to taste with salt and pepper.
6. Bake in slow oven (325°F to 350°F) until the mixture thickens.

GREEN BEANS WITH ALMONDS

Yield: 4 servings

Exchange 1 serving for: 1 Vegetable Exchange List 2B
and 1 Fat Exchange

Ingredients: 2 cups hot cooked green beans
2 tsps. butter or margarine
12 blanched almonds, slivered

Method: 1. Toss butter or margarine and almonds with the cooked green beans.
2. Serve hot.

GREEN BEANS WITH PIMENTO

Yield: 4 servings

Exchange 1 serving for: 1 Vegetable Exchange List 2B

Ingredients: 2 cups hot cooked green beans
1 tbsp. finely chopped pimento

Method: 1. Toss chopped pimento with green beans just before serving.
2. Serve hot.

HARVARD BEETS

Yield: 4 servings

Exchange 1 serving for: 1 Vegetable Exchange List 2A

Ingredients: 2 cups cooked and drained, fresh or canned beets
¼ tsp. salt
f.g. pepper
½ tbsp. cornstarch
¼ cup vinegar
⅓ cup water
1½ tsps. artificial liquid sweetener

Method: 1. Cut beets in slices or cubes.
2. Mix cornstarch, salt and pepper with cold water and vinegar. Cook until thick, stirring constantly.
3. Add beets and artificial liquid sweetener; let stand ½ hour, keeping the mixture hot until serving time.

CABBAGE

Cabbage may be steamed or boiled until just tender. Do not overcook. It may be served plain or in any of the following ways:

CABBAGE SERVED WITH BUTTER, MARGARINE, BACON, OR BACON FAT

Yield: 1 serving

Exchange for: 1 Vegetable Exchange List 2B
and 1 Fat Exchange

Allow ½ cup cooked cabbage per serving, and 1 strip crisp bacon crumbled or 1 tsp. butter, margarine, or bacon fat.

CABBAGE WITH CREAM

Yield: 1 serving

Exchange for: 1 Vegetable Exchange List 2B
and 1 Fat Exchange

Ingredients: ½ cup cooked cabbage
2 tbsps. coffee cream (18%)
salt and pepper to taste

Method: 1. Add cream and seasonings to the hot cooked cabbage.
2. Reheat and serve.

CABBAGE AU GRATIN

Yield: 4 servings

Exchange 1 serving for: 1 Vegetable Exchange List 2A
and 1 Milk Exchange
and 1 Fat Exchange

Ingredients: 4 tsps. butter or margarine
2½ tbsps. flour
2 cups whole milk
½ tsp. salt
f.g. pepper
2 cups drained, cooked cabbage
4 tbsps. grated cheese

Method: 1. Melt butter or margarine in the top of a double boiler.
2. Add flour and blend until smooth.
3. Gradually add hot milk; stir and cook until there is no taste of raw starch.
4. Add salt, pepper and cooked cabbage; mix well.
5. Place in baking dish.
6. Sprinkle grated cheese over cabbage and milk mixture.
7. Bake uncovered at 375°F until the mixture is piping hot and the cheese has melted and started to brown (about 20 minutes).

SWEET AND SOUR CABBAGE

Yield: 6 servings

Exchange 1 serving for: 1 Vegetable Exchange List 2B
and 1 Fat Exchange

Ingredients: 2 tbsps. bacon fat
4 tbsps. vinegar
1 small head cabbage
salt and pepper to taste
1 tsp. finely chopped onion, if desired
1 tsp. artificial liquid sweetener, if desired

Method: 1. Heat bacon fat and vinegar together in frying pan until very hot.
2. While this is heating, cut head of cabbage in half. Take out the core and shred cabbage very fine.
3. Turn the heat under the fat and vinegar very low.
4. Add the shredded cabbage, salt, pepper and onion to the fat and vinegar.
5. Put lid on the frying pan and let the mixture simmer until cabbage is tender.
6. Add artificial liquid sweetener about 5 minutes before end of cooking; serve hot.

GERMAN SOUR RED CABBAGE

Yield: 6 servings

Exchange 1 serving for: 1 Vegetable Exchange List 2B
and 1 Fat Exchange

Ingredients: 2 tbsps. butter or margarine
6 cups raw shredded red cabbage
1 medium onion sliced in rings
½ cup vinegar
¼ cup water
1 tsp. artificial liquid sweetener

Method: 1. Melt butter in large saucepan.
2. Add shredded raw cabbage using only the water that clings to leaves after washing.
3. Cook covered over low heat until tender (about 3 minutes).
4. Add onion rings, vinegar and water.
5. Cook covered over low heat (7 to 10 minutes).
6. Add sweetener to liquid and carefully spoon over the cooked cabbage.
7. Season to taste.

CAULIFLOWER WITH CHEESE SAUCE

Yield: 1 serving

Exchange for: 1 Vegetable Exchange List 2B
and 1 Fat Exchange

Ingredients: ½ cup hot cooked drained cauliflower
1 tsp. processed cheese spread

Method: 1. Mix cheese spread with hot cauliflower and serve.
or Place cheese on top of hot cauliflower at serving time.

CAULIFLOWER AU GRATIN

Yield: 4 servings

Exchange 1 serving for: 1 Vegetable Exchange List 2A
and 1 Milk Exchange
and 1 Fat Exchange

See CABBAGE AU GRATIN page 22.
Use 2 cups cooked drained cauliflower in place of 2 cups cooked drained cabbage.

CARROTS

The flavour and texture of carrots blend well with other vegetables. Some interesting combinations are:

1. Carrots with peas, mixed and seasoned with a pinch of thyme or mint.
   Exchange ⅓ cup for: 1 Vegetable Exchange List 2A

2. Carrots and parsnips cooked together.
   Exchange ⅓ cup for: 1 Vegetable Exchange List 2A

3. Carrots and celery cooked together.
   Exchange ½ cup for: 1 Vegetable Exchange List 2A

4. Carrots served with chopped parsley, watercress or chives are both attractive and tasty.
   Exchange ½ cup for: 1 Vegetable Exchange List 2A

CELERY CREOLE

Yield: 4 servings

Exchange 1 serving for: 1 Vegetable Exchange List 2A
and 1 Fat Exchange

Ingredients: 4 strips side bacon
½ medium-sized cooking onion, chopped
½ tbsp. chopped green pepper
2 cups celery, cut in 1½″-2″ lengths
2 cups canned tomatoes
salt and pepper to taste

Method: 1. Cut bacon into small pieces.

2. Fry until crisp; remove from pan to a paper towel.

3. Drain fat from pan; return 4 tsps. fat to pan.

4. Cook chopped onion and green pepper lightly in fat.

5. Combine celery, bacon, onion and green pepper in baking dish.

6. Add canned tomatoes and seasoning as desired.

7. Bake in moderate oven (350°F to 375°F) until the celery is tender and mixture has thickened (about 25 minutes).

CREAMED CELERY

Yield: 4 servings

Exchange 1 serving for: 1 Vegetable Exchange List 2B
and ½ Milk Exchange
and 1 Fat Exchange

Ingredients: 4 tsps. butter or margarine
4 tsps. flour
1 cup whole milk
salt and pepper to taste
2 cups cooked celery cut in 1″-2″ pieces

Method: 1. Melt butter or margarine in top of a double boiler.
2. Add flour and blend until smooth.
3. Gradually add the hot milk, stirring constantly to avoid lumps.
4. Cook over hot water until there is no taste of raw starch, stirring frequently.
5. Add cooked celery and seasonings; mix well and reheat.

Note: 1 tbsp. grated cheese may be added to the sauce without appreciably changing the food value.

BRAISED CELERY

Yield: 4 servings

Exchange 1 serving for: 1 Vegetable Exchange List 2B
and 1 Fat Exchange

Ingredients: 2 hearts of celery
4 tsps. butter or margarine, melted
salt and pepper to taste
1 cup tomato juice

Method: 1. Wash and cut 2 hearts of celery in half, lengthwise, allowing one half celery heart (about 3″ to 4″ in length) for each serving.
2. Place in baking pan.
3. Dribble melted fat and seasonings over the celery.
4. Add tomato juice.
5. Place in oven preheated to 375°F.
6. Bake 45 to 50 minutes, or until tender; baste 2 or 3 times during the cooking. If the liquid cooks away, add water or consommé.

CORN, MEXICAN STYLE

Yield: 4 servings

Exchange 1 serving for: 1 Vegetable Exchange List 2A
and 1 Fat Exchange

Ingredients: 4 tsps. butter or margarine
1 tbsp. chopped red and/or green pepper
1 tsp. chopped onion
½ cup plus 2 tbsps. corn kernels

Method: 1. Cook chopped pepper and onion in butter or margarine until onion is golden brown.
2. Add the corn and mix well.
3. Reheat and serve.

Note: For larger servings of corn allow 1¼ cups corn kernels, but keep the other ingredients the same as above.
Exchange 1 serving for: 1 Bread Exchange
and 1 Fat Exchange

CORN PUDDING

Yield: 6 servings

Exchange 1 serving for: 1 Vegetable Exchange List 2A
and 1 Milk Exchange
and 1 Fat Exchange

Ingredients: 2 cups canned corn (cream style)
½ tsp. artificial liquid sweetener, if desired
1 tsp. salt
f.g. pepper
2 eggs, slightly beaten
2 tbsps. melted butter or margarine
2 cups hot whole milk

Method: 1. Add seasonings and artificial liquid sweetener to the corn.
2. Add eggs slightly beaten, then melted butter or margarine, and milk.
3. Pour into a slightly greased baking dish.
4. Place baking dish in a pan with about 1″ hot water in it.
5. Oven-poach until firm in oven at 325°F.

BRAISED ONIONS

Yield: 4 servings

Exchange 1 serving for: 1 Vegetable Exchange List 2A
and 1 Fat Exchange
and 1 Calorie Poor Food List B

Ingredients: 4 medium-sized onions, peeled
1½ cups canned tomatoes, or tomato juice
salt and pepper to taste
4 tsps. butter or margarine

Method:
1. Parboil onions about 10 minutes.
2. Drain, reserving ½ cup liquid.
3. Place onions in baking dish; mix liquid (reserved from cooking onions) with the canned tomatoes or tomato juice and seasonings.
4. Pour over and around onions.
5. Cut a small hollow in each onion and put 1 tsp. of butter or margarine in each.
6. Bake at 350°F to 375°F, basting frequently until onions are tender (about 30 minutes).

EGG PLANT CREOLE

Yield: 4 servings

Exchange 1 serving for: 1 Vegetable Exchange List 2A
and 1 Vegetable Exchange List 2B

Ingredients: 8 slices egg plant (about 4″ x 4″ x 1″ thick)
1 tbsp. finely chopped onion
1 tbsp. finely chopped celery
2 cups canned tomatoes
salt and pepper to taste

Method:
1. Pare each slice of egg plant and sprinkle with salt.
2. Lay slice upon slice and place on a plate or in a bowl. Place a plate on top for a weight and let stand 1 to 2 hours.
3. Drain; cut into cubes if desired, and place in a baking dish.
4. Add chopped onion, celery, canned tomatoes and seasonings; bake in moderate oven (350°F to 375°F) until tender (about 30 minutes).

PEAS

Green peas may be served in many of the same ways as green beans. The size of serving, however, is smaller due to the higher starch content of peas.

If you use canned green peas, the size serving for 1 Vegetable Exchange List 2A is ¼ cup. For fresh green peas, or fresh frozen green peas, the size serving for 1 Vegetable Exchange List 2A is ⅓ cup. With this in mind, there are many interesting ways to serve green peas.

Minted Green Peas: A little mint, fresh or dried, added to fresh green peas or frozen green peas while cooking, is a must in many households. The mint is a Calorie Free Food.

Green Peas with Pimento: Mix ½ tsp. chopped pimento with the serving of peas allowed. The pimento is a Calorie Free Food.

GREEN PEAS WITH MUSHROOMS

Yield: 1 serving

Exchange for: 1 Vegetable Exchange List 2A
and 1 Fat Exchange
and 1 Calorie Free Food List A

Ingredients: 4 mushroom caps, sliced
1 tsp. butter or margarine
⅓ cup fresh or frozen green peas, cooked,
or ¼ cup canned green peas

Method: 1. Lightly cook the mushrooms in the butter or margarine.
2. Toss mushrooms and butter or margarine with the hot cooked or canned peas.

STUFFED GREEN PEPPER

Yield: 1 serving

Exchange for: 1 Vegetable Exchange List 2B
and 1 Bread Exchange

Ingredients: 1 small green pepper
3 level tbsps. cooked, drained rice
or ½ slice bread, cubed
1 tsp. chopped onion
1 tsp. chopped celery
salt and pepper
⅓ cup tomato juice

Method: 1. Wash and cut stem end from green pepper, and remove seeds and membrane.

2. Place in pan with ½″ to 1″ water in the bottom.

3. Mix cooked rice **or** bread cubes, chopped onion, celery, salt, pepper and tomato juice together.

4. Fill green pepper with the rice **or** bread mixture.

5. Bake in oven at 350°F until the green pepper is tender (about 20 minutes).

ESCALLOPED POTATOES

Yield: 1 serving

Exchange 1 serving for: 1 Bread Exchange
and 1 Milk Exchange
and 1 Fat Exchange

Ingredients: 1 small potato, peeled
salt and pepper
½ tsp. chopped onion (optional)
½ cup whole milk
1 tsp. butter or margarine

Method: 1. Slice peeled potato into thin slices.

2. Place a thin layer (half) of potato slices on bottom of an individual casserole dish.

3. Sprinkle lightly with salt, pepper, and the chopped onion.

4. Cover with remaining potato slices.

5. Sprinkle with salt and pepper.

6. Add milk.

7. Dot top with butter or margarine.

8. Bake in moderate oven (350°F) until potatoes are tender.

Note: If the fat allowance is very low, use ½ cup skim milk instead of ½ cup whole milk. The exchange would then be:
1 Bread Exchange
and 1 Milk Exchange

POTATO PANCAKES

Yield: 8 pancakes or 4 servings

Exchange 2 pancakes for: 1 Bread Exchange
and 1 Calorie Poor Food List B

Ingredients: 4 small potatoes, peeled
1 egg, well beaten
1 tbsp. flour
1 tbsp. chopped onion
salt and pepper to taste

Method: 1. Cook and mash potatoes.
2. Add egg, flour, onion, salt and pepper; mix well.
3. Form into 8 flat cakes.
4. Place on slightly greased baking sheet.
5. Bake in moderate oven (350°F) for 20 to 30 minutes, or until brown.

MASHED POTATO PUDDING

Yield: 6 servings

Exchange 1 serving for: 1 Bread Exchange
and ½ Meat Exchange

Ingredients: 2 cups hot mashed potatoes
salt and pepper to taste
1 tsp. grated or finely chopped onion
1 tbsp. chopped parsley
2 tbsps. butter or margarine
2 tbsps. whole milk
2 eggs, separated
paprika

Method: 1. To the two cups hot mashed potato, add salt and pepper to taste, onion, parsley, butter or margarine and milk.
2. Beat together well with electric beater or potato masher.
3. Add egg yolks which have been beaten until light and fluffy.
4. Mix thoroughly with the potato mixture.
5. Fold in the stiffly beaten egg whites.
6. Place in a shallow, lightly greased pan; sprinkle with paprika, and bake in moderate oven (350°F) for 30 to 40 minutes, until the potatoes are light golden brown.
7. Serve immediately, cutting into 6 equal portions.

STUFFED BAKED POTATO

Yield: 4 servings

Exchange 1 serving for: 1 Bread Exchange
and 1 Fat Exchange

Ingredients: 4 small potatoes, skins on
salt and pepper
½ tsp. grated onion
4 tsps. butter or margarine
1 egg white, beaten until stiff
paprika

Method:
1. Scrub 4 small potatoes of uniform size.
2. Pierce skins with a fork.
3. Bake until tender in hot oven (400°F to 425°F).
4. Remove from oven; slice thin top from each potato, lengthwise.
5. Remove cooked potato from skins, leaving skins intact.
6. Mash potato; add salt, pepper, grated onion, 2 tsps. butter or margarine and mix well.
7. Fold in stiffy beaten egg white.
8. Pile the potato mixture back into the four potato shells, dividing the mixture equally.
9. Sprinkle with paprika and dot with remaining butter or margarine; return to oven until thoroughly heated, and slightly browned.

MASHED SQUASH

Yield: 4 servings

Exchange 1 serving for: 1 Vegetable Exchange List 2A
and 1 Fat Exchange

Ingredients: 2 cups hot cooked mashed squash
4 tsps. butter or margarine
½ tsp. artificial liquid sweetener, if desired
salt and pepper to taste
¼ tsp. ground cinnamon

Method:
1. To the hot mashed squash, add the other ingredients and mix well.

Note: If desired, a few drops of lemon juice may be added.

SQUASH BAKED OR STEAMED IN THE SHELL

Yield: 2 servings

Exchange ½ cup mashed squash for: 1 Vegetable Exchange List 2A
and 1 Fat Exchange

Method: 1. Wash and cut one squash in half or quarters.
2. Rub 1 tsp. butter or margarine over cut edges of each serving.
3. Sprinkle with salt and pepper.
4. Bake in hot oven (400°F) about 40 minutes or until tender; or steam over boiling water until tender.
5. Remove squash from shell; mash and season to taste; reheat if necessary.

BAKED TOMATO

Yield: 1 serving

Exchange for: 1 Vegetable Exchange List 2B

Ingredients: 1 medium-sized tomato
salt and pepper
other seasonings to taste, such as a sprinkling of basil, thyme; ½ tsp. chopped onion; chopped parsley; sage or chives

Method: 1. Wash tomato and cut out the stem end.
2. Place in a small baking dish with a little water in the bottom (about ½″).
3. Sprinkle with seasonings of choice.
4. Bake in moderate oven (350°F) until tomato is just tender, but not so soft it will fall apart (15 to 20 minutes).

ESCALLOPED TOMATOES

Yield: 4 servings

Exchange 1 serving for: 1 Vegetable Exchange List 2A
and 1 Fat Exchange

Ingredients: 1 tsp. chopped onion
4 tsps. butter or margarine
1½ cups canned tomatoes
1 slice bread
salt and pepper to taste

Method: 1. Cook onion slightly in butter or margarine.
2. Add tomatoes, bread cut in small cubes, salt and pepper.
3. Heat thoroughly.

BROILED ITALIAN STYLE TOMATOES

Yield: 4 servings

Exchange 1 serving for: 1 Vegetable Exchange List 2B

Ingredients: 4 medium-sized firm ripe tomatoes
f.g. salt
¼ tsp. oregano or sweet basil, crushed
2 tbsps. commercial low calorie Italian or French dressing

Method: 1. Core tomatoes and cut in half crosswise.
2. Arrange on broiler pan.
3. Season cut surfaces with salt and pepper and sprinkle with oregano.
4. Pour the dressing over the cut surfaces evenly.
5. Broil cut sides up, 3 inches from heat about 5 minutes or until heated thoroughly.
6. Remove carefully to serving plates; two halves per serving.

ZUCCHINI WITH TOMATOES AU GRATIN

Yield: 8 servings

Exchange 1 serving for: 1 Vegetable Exchange List 2A
and 1 Fat Exchange

Ingredients: 2 lbs. zucchini
½ medium onion, chopped
2 tbsps. butter or margarine
2 cups stewed tomatoes
½ tsp. salt
f.g. pepper
½ cup grated Parmesan cheese

Method: 1. Wash zucchini and cut into ¼ inch slices.
2. Cook onion in butter or margarine; add zucchini and cook slowly 5 minutes, stirring frequently.
3. Add tomatoes, salt and pepper.
4. Cover and cook 5 minutes longer.
5. Turn into lightly greased casserole or baking dish.
6. Sprinkle cheese over the top.
7. Bake at 375°F for 20 minutes.

33

ZUCCHINI PANCAKE

Yield: 8 servings

Exchange 1 serving for: 1 Vegetable Exchange List 2B
and 1 Meat Exchange
and 1 Fat Exchange

Ingredients: 1½ lbs. zucchini
4 tbsps. salad oil
1 medium onion, chopped
1 green pepper, chopped
1 tbsp. dry parsley flakes
8 oz. tomato sauce (commercial)
1 tsp. basil
1 tsp. oregano
4 eggs
½ cup whole milk
salt and pepper to taste
½ cup grated Parmesan cheese
paprika to garnish

Method:
1. Wash and slice zucchini in ¼ inch slices.
2. Heat oil in ovenproof 10 inch casserole or iron frying pan.
3. Add zucchini, onion, green pepper and parsley.
4. Cook zucchini mixture until lightly browned.
5. Add tomato sauce, basil and oregano.
6. Simmer over low heat until mixture is moist, but not soupy.
7. Beat eggs; add milk, salt and pepper. Pour over hot zucchini mixture.
8. Cover and cook over low heat until eggs are set (about 7 minutes).
9. Sprinkle with grated cheese and paprika.
10. Slip under broiler until cheese is melted, and starting to brown.
11. Cut in wedges and serve hot.

MEAT, FISH AND POULTRY

Dieter's Grace

> Now I sit me down to eat,
> I pray the Lord I will not cheat,
> If I should reach for cake or bread,
> Please guide my hand to meat instead.

Anonymous

Meat, fish and poultry are excellent sources of high quality protein, and are rich in many important minerals and vitamins. These foods are particularly important to the diabetic, since they provide one of the main sources of protein in the meal pattern.

CARE AND HANDLING:

These foods are highly perishable. To preserve both flavour and nutritive values, they should be handled carefully from the time they are purchased until they are served. Because they are particularly susceptible to spoilage and to food poisoning bacteria, meat, fish and poultry should be prepared, cooked and served in sanitary surroundings, and should be protected from contamination and heat during storage.

Always remove the store wrappings from meat and poultry when you return from shopping. Since both meat and poultry tend to absorb other flavours, they should be rewrapped or covered during storage. For freezer storage, the wrapping should be moisture-vapour-proof material.

Whether raw or cooked, **meat** and **poultry** should be kept in the coldest part of the refrigerator or in the freezer. It is preferable to thaw frozen meat or poultry before cooking, and if time permits, the thawing should be done in the refrigerator. Once thawed, raw meat or poultry should be cooked as soon as possible. Although raw meat or poultry should not be refrozen, once these foods are cooked, they may be frozen again for further storage.

Fish should be well wrapped or tightly covered if stored in the refrigerator, to protect other foods from fish flavours. Frozen fish may be cooked without pre-thawing, but additional time should be allowed. Once thawed, raw or cooked fish should not be refrozen.

COOKING:

Meat: As a general rule, low temperatures are recommended to reduce shrinkage, improve flavour, retain juices, and produce an even degree of "doneness." Dry heat may be used for tender cuts of meat; less tender cuts should be cooked by moist heat. The method of cooking will depend upon the cut and quality of meat purchased.

An oven temperature of 325°F is recommended. For best results, roast the meat uncovered and use a meat thermometer. Pierce the meat with a skewer or an ice pick, and push the bulb of the thermometer into the thickest part of the roast, away from bone or fat. (See Roasting Table for times and temperature readings.)

Poultry: As with meats, there are many methods of cooking poultry. Again, low temperatures are recommended to produce tender, moist, flavourful meat, and to reduce shrinkage to a minimum.

Except for very small birds, which require slightly higher temperatures, an oven temperature of 325°F is recommended. A meat thermometer is the surest guide to "doneness." It should be inserted into the centre of the dressing in a stuffed bird, or into the centre of a thick muscle on the inside of a thigh in an unstuffed bird. Be sure the thermometer does not rest on a bone. (See Roasting Table for times and temperature readings.)

Fish: All fish should be cooked gently, but quickly. Temperatures ranging from 400°F to 450°F are recommended for baking. Most kinds of fish may be baked, broiled or pan broiled. Fish with stronger flavours may be simmered in moist heat. To test fish, flake it gently with a fork. If it flakes easily, it is cooked.

COOKING TERMS AND DEFINITIONS

Bake: to cook by dry heat, usually in an oven. This process is called **roasting** when applied to meat.

Barbecue: to roast by direct heat on a spit, over coals, or in an oven broiler, basting frequently with sauce.

Baste: to moisten food during cooking with liquid fat drippings, or other liquid, by ladling the liquid over the food.

Boil: to cook in liquid at boiling temperature (212°F at sea level). The word is sometimes wrongly used to describe "simmering", as in the case of "boiled" eggs or ham.

Braise: to brown meat or vegetables in a small amount of hot fat and then cover and cook slowly, either in the juices, or in a small amount of added liquid, in the oven or on top of the stove.

Broil: to cook by direct heat, under a broiler unit or burner, or over an open fire. Also referred to as **grilling.**

Dredge: to coat with a dry ingredient such as flour or salt, by sprinkling, dipping or rolling.

Fricassee: to cook by braising, often with the addition of a sauce.

Fry, Pan-Fry: to cook in a small amount of hot fat or oil in a shallow pan. Sometimes referred to as **sautéing.**

Grill: see **broil.**

Marinate: to let stand in a liquid, usually an oil and acid mixture such as French dressing, until seasoned.

Pan-Broil: to cook uncovered, in a hot shallow pan ungreased or lightly greased, pouring off fat as it accumulates.

Poach: to cook gently in liquid at simmering temperature (just below boiling) so that food retains its shape.

Oven Poach: to bake, with baking pan placed in a shallow pan of water to slow the baking process and avoid curdling.

Roast: see **bake.**

Sauté: see **pan-fry.**

Sear: to brown the surface of meat by short application of intense heat, to improve appearance, develop flavour and seal in juices.

Simmer: to cook in liquid just below boiling point; the surface of the liquid should barely ripple.

Steam: to cook covered, directly over boiling water, or in a tightly covered utensil in which steam is circulating.

Stew: to simmer or boil in a small quantity of liquid. For meats, simmering temperature is always used.

ROASTING TABLE FOR MEATS AND POULTRY

Food	Description	Oven Temp.	Minutes per lb.	Interior Thermometer Reading
Beef	rare	325°F	20 to 30	130°F to 140°F
	medium	325°F	25 to 35	140°F to 150°F
	well done	325°F	30 to 40	150°F to 170°F
Lamb	leg with bone	325°F	25 to 30	180°F
	shoulder, rolled	325°F	35 to 40	180°F
Pork	loin, centre cut	325°F	35 to 45	185°F
	shoulder, rolled	325°F	55 to 60	185°F
Veal	leg	325°F	35 to 45	180°F
	shoulder, rolled	325°F	50 to 55	180°F
Duck		325°F	30 to 35	190°F (in meat)
Chicken	roasting	325°F	30 to 45	165°F (in stuffing) 190°F (in thigh)
Turkey	8 to 10 lbs.	325°F	30 to 35	for all weights:
	10 to 16 lbs.	325°F	28 to 30	160°F (in stuffing)
	18 to 25 lbs.	325°F	25 to 28	190°F (in thigh)

Note: The number of minutes per pound indicated for each food is merely a guide. The surest test that your meat or poultry has reached the desired degree of doneness is by using a meat thermometer. The interior thermometer readings given in the table indicate well done meat or poultry unless otherwise noted.

HERBS AND SEASONINGS

A variety of herbs and seasonings can vary the flavour of meats, poultry, fish and other dishes in a most delicious sense. Do not be afraid to experiment with your favourite combinations of herbs and spices. Keep the following tips in mind:

— Purchase in small amounts and keep in tightly covered containers.

— Test for freshness from time to time, especially those not used often.

— Use sparingly. Excessive amounts will mask the flavour of the food you are trying to improve.

— Add seasonings and herbs during latter part of cooking time, to improve flavour and develop aroma.

— Tie mixed herbs and seasonings in a small cheesecloth bag, so they may be removed easily after cooking.

— Choose one predominate flavour, and blend others with it.

— Monosodium glutamate (M.S.G.) will enhance the flavour of any meat dish. Use about 1 teaspoon per pound of meat, during cooking.

The following suggestions will help you to season your foods expertly:

With Roast Beef: basil; coriander; rosemary; bay leaf; dill; thyme; horseradish; mustard.

With Beef and Veal Stews: bay leaf; thyme; sage; parsley; garlic; marjoram; summer savoury; grated lemon rind; celery seed.

With Boiled Beef: horseradish; thyme; cloves.

With Pork: caraway; sage; basil; savoury; fennel.

With Ham: nutmeg; mace; coriander; cinnamon; cloves; mustard.

With Liver: basil; thyme.

With Chicken: lemon; paprika; orange; thyme; chives; rosemary; chervil; bay leaf; parsley; celery; caraway; marjoram.

With Fish: anise (shellfish); celery; capers; green pepper; lemon.

Note: Many herbs and seasonings are sold powdered or salted. Herb salts and monosodium glutamate must be omitted from foods for diets restricted in salt or sodium.

SPICED POT ROAST

Yield: 8 servings

Exchange one 3-oz. serving or 3 slices each measuring 4" x 2" x ¼"
for: 3 Meat Exchanges

Ingredients: 2 lbs. boneless chuck beef
1 medium onion, sliced
1 bay leaf
salt, pepper, vinegar, water
1 tsp. whole pepper berries

Method: 1. Rub meat with salt and pepper and place in an earthenware or glass bowl.
2. Add onion, bay leaf, and whole pepper berries.
3. Marinate meat in equal parts of vinegar and water for 24 hours. Drain and reserve liquid.
4. Place meat in roasting pan; sear well; add 3 tbsps. spiced vinegar mixture.
5. Cover and cook slowly at 325°F for 1½ hours.

SWISS STEAK

Yield: 4 servings

Exchange 1 serving for: 3 Meat Exchanges

Ingredients: 1 lb. round steak
2 medium onions, sliced
2 tsps. vinegar
½ cup celery, diced
seasonings to taste

Method: 1. Trim round steak and portion into 4 equal servings. Pound to break down tissue.
2. Sear meat on both sides.
3. Cover with water; add remaining ingredients.
4. Continue cooking in oven or on stove. (About 1-1½ hrs.)

Variation: 2 cups tomato juice may be used in place of water.

BEEF STEW

Yield: 4 servings

Exchange 1 serving for: 3 Meat Exchanges
and 1 Vegetable Exchange List 2A
and 1 Bread Exchange

Ingredients: 1 lb. lean cubed beef
¼ cup sliced onions
2 bay leaves
6 small whole carrots
4 small potatoes, peeled

Method: 1. Cube beef in 1½″ cubes; sear on all sides.
2. Cover meat with boiling water; add onions and bay leaves; cover pot and simmer for 1½ hours.
3. Add vegetables and cook ½ hour longer.

FRENCH CANADIAN TOURTIERE

Yield: 6 servings

Exchange 1 serving for: 1 Bread Exchange
and 2 Fat Exchanges
and 2 Meat Exchanges

Ingredients: Pastry:
1 cup flour
⅓ cup lard
¼ tsp. salt
2 tbsps. ice water (appproximately)

Method: 1. Mix flour and salt.
2. Cut in lard. Sprinkle in ice water and mix lightly.
3. Roll on lightly floured board.
4. Line 8″ pie plate or 6 individual tart shells with pastry, reserving enough for thin cover.

Ingredients: Filling:
½ lb. lean ground pork
½ lb. lean ground beef
¼ cup chopped onions
¼ tsp. nutmeg
¼ tsp. cinnamon
¼ tsp. cloves
¼ tsp. salt
¼ tsp. pepper
¼ cup beef broth (fat removed)

Method: 1. Cook meat over low heat with onion and spices; add broth.
2. Fill unbaked pastry shell or tart shells, and cover with thin layer of pastry; use ½ cup filling for each individual shell.
3. Bake at 400°F about 25 minutes or until golden brown.

Note: 1. Serve with 1 tsp. catsup and/or sour pickles; see Calorie Poor Foods List B.
2. Tourtieres can be made in advance and frozen before baking; do not thaw before baking; bake at 400°F approximately 35 minutes.

MEAT PATTY

Yield: 1 meat patty
Exchange for: 3 Meat Exchanges
Ingredients: 9 tbsps. lean minced beef (½ cup + 1 tbsp.)
grated onion to taste
salt, pepper, sage, thyme and garlic salt to taste
Method: 1. Add seasonings and onion to meat and form into 1 patty.
2. Broil or fry in part of fat allowance. If cooking on top of stove, add a little water when meat is seared to avoid sticking.

BACON BURGERS

Yield: 4 servings
Exchange 1 serving for: 3 Meat Exchanges
and 1 Fat Exchange
Ingredients: 4 strips bacon
¾ lb. lean minced beef
¼ lb. lean minced pork
1 tbsp. chopped parsley
1 tbsp. chopped onion
⅛ tsp. each thyme, mace, sage, savoury
1 tbsp. green pepper, chopped
¾ tsp. salt
¼ tsp. pepper
Method: 1. Combine all ingredients, except bacon.
2. Shape into 4 patties.
3. Broil 5 minutes on each side and continue cooking to desired degree of doneness. Broil bacon at the same time.
4. Garnish meat patties with crisp bacon slices.

BAKED STUFFED TOMATOES

Yield: 4 servings
Exchange 1 serving for: 2 Meat Exchanges
and 1 Vegetable Exchange List 2A
Ingredients: 4 medium sized tomatoes
¾ lb. minced beef
1 tbsp. grated onion
1 tbsp. chopped parsley
1 tsp. Worcestershire sauce
salt and pepper to taste
¼ cup bread crumbs
¼ cup grated cheese

Method: 1. Remove stem ends of tomatoes; scoop out some of the pulp and drain tomatoes.
2. Combine beef, tomato pulp and seasonings; stuff tomato shells with the mixture, dividing it evenly.
3. Sprinkle with mixture of bread crumbs and grated cheese.
4. Place in baking dish and bake at 375°F for 30 minutes.

BASIC MEAT LOAF

Yield: 4 servings

Exchange 1 serving for: 3 Meat Exchanges

Ingredients: 1 lb. lean minced beef
1 egg, slightly beaten
1 tbsp. chopped onion
½ tsp. salt
¼ tsp. pepper

Method: 1. Mix ingredients and mould into loaf pan.
2. Bake at 375°F for 30 to 45 minutes.

SEASONED MEAT LOAF

Yield: 4 servings

Exchange 1 serving for: 3 Meat Exchanges
and 1 Vegetable Exchange List 2B

Ingredients: 1 lb. lean minced beef
2 tbsps. minced green pepper
1 tbsp. chopped onion
1½ cups tomato juice
¼ tsp. Worcestershire sauce
½ tsp. artificial liquid sweetener
½ tsp. salt
¼ tsp. pepper

Method: 1. Mix ingredients and mould into loaf pan.
2. Bake at 375°F for 30 to 45 minutes.

BEEF PORCUPINES

Yield: 4 servings

Exchange 1 serving for: 3 Meat Exchanges
and 1 Vegetable Exchange List 2A
and 1 Bread Exchange

Ingredients: 1 lb. lean minced beef
1 tsp. baking powder
1 medium-sized onion, grated
1 tbsp. chopped parsley
⅓ cup skim milk
1 tsp. salt
¼ tsp. black pepper
⅓ cup washed, drained, uncooked rice
¼ tsp. thyme
⅛ tsp. cloves
⅛ tsp. poultry seasoning
1 tsp. Worcestershire sauce
half 10 oz. tin tomato soup, undiluted
¾ cup water

Method: 1. Mix all ingredients except soup and water; form into patties and place in baking dish.
2. Mix soup and water and pour over patties.
3. Bake uncovered, in a moderate oven (350°F) for 35 minutes; cover and continue baking for 30 minutes.

CABBAGE ROLLS

Yield: 8 cabbage rolls or 4 servings

Exchange 1 serving (2 rolls) for: 2 Meat Exchanges
and 1 Vegetable Exchange List 2A

Ingredients: 8 large cabbage leaves
¾ lb. lean minced beef
½ cup cooked rice
¼ cup finely chopped onion
1½ tbsps. finely chopped parsley
½ tsp. thyme
½ tsp. salt
¼ tsp. pepper
½ cup tomato juice

(Cabbage Rolls Cont'd)

Method: 1. Cook cabbage leaves just until limp (1-2 mins.); drain.
2. Brown minced beef; drain off excess fat.
3. Combine meat, rice, onion, seasonings and tomato juice.
4. Divide meat mixture into 8 equal portions; place each portion in centre of a cabbage leaf.
5. Wrap each tightly and fasten with wooden toothpicks.
6. Arrange cabbage rolls in casserole dish; add extra tomato juice or broth to keep rolls moist during baking.
7. Bake in moderate oven (325°F) until tender (30 mins.).

Note: This filling may be used to stuff green peppers as well.

BURGER KABOBS

Yield: 4 kabobs or 4 servings
Exchange 1 kabob for: 3 Meat Exchanges
and 1 Vegetable Exchange List 2A
Ingredients: 1 large green pepper, cut in 8 pieces
4 small onions, each cut in half
1 lb. lean minced beef
¾ tsp. monosodium glutamate
¾ tsp. salt
¼ tsp. pepper
Method: 1. Mix minced beef and spices; shape into 12 meat balls.
2. Thread 3 meat balls, 2 pieces green pepper and 2 onion halves, alternately on each 4 skewers.
3. Cook over barbecue or broil, turning often until meat is done.

NEW ENGLAND BOILED DINNER (one-dish meal)

Yield: 8 servings
Exchange 1 serving for: 3 Meat Exchanges
and 1 Vegetable Exchange List 2A
and 1 Vegetable Exchange List 2B
and ½ Bread Exchange
Ingredients: 2 lbs. lean corned beef or boiling beef
4 whole small carrots
1 cup diced turnip
4 small potatoes, peeled
4 wedges cabbage
4 small onions
salt and pepper to taste

45

Method:　1.　Cover beef with cold water and bring to a boil.

2.　Simmer in tightly covered pan for 1 hour.

3.　Add all vegetables except cabbage and simmer ½ hour.

4.　Add cabbage and cook uncovered for 15 minutes.

LIVER BAKED IN FOIL

Yield: 1 serving

Exchange for:　3 Meat Exchanges
and 1 Vegetable Exchange List 2B

Ingredients:　one 4 oz. portion beef or calves liver
⅓ cup tomato juice
salt and pepper

Method:　1.　Place liver on centre of a piece of cooking foil in casserole.

2.　Season with salt and pepper.

3.　Pour tomato juice over liver.

4.　Seal the foil carefully.

5.　Bake in moderate oven (350°F) for 45 minutes.

BAKED HAM SLICE — MUSTARD SAUCE

Yield: 4 servings

Exchange 1 serving for:　3 Meat Exchanges
and 1 Calorie Poor Food List B

Ingredients:　1 lb. ham slice, about 1″ thick
½ tsp. artificial liquid sweetener
¼ tsp. mustard
¼ tsp. Worcestershire sauce
2 tbsps. water
½ cup unsweetened pineapple juice
pinch of salt
pinch of paprika

Method:　1.　Blend seasonings with pineapple juice and water and pour over ham slice.

2.　Bake in moderate oven (350°F) for 20 to 30 minutes.

BAKED HAM PATTIES

Yield: 4 servings

Exchange 1 serving for: 2 Meat Exchanges
and ½ Fruit Exchange

Ingredients: 1 egg
2 cups minced cooked ham
1 tsp. chopped onion
seasonings to taste
4 slices unsweetened canned pineapple
4 tbsps. unsweetened pineapple juice

Method: 1. Add beaten egg to minced ham and chopped onion.
2. Season to taste.
3. Form into 4 patties of equal size.
4. Halve the pineapple slices; place four halves on baking sheet; top each with ham patty; place remaining pineapple slices on top of ham patties.
5. Pour the pineapple juice over patties.
6. Bake in moderate oven (350°F) for 15 minutes.

BAKED SPARERIBS

Yield: 4 servings

Exchange 1 serving for: 3 Meat Exchanges
and 1 Calorie Poor Food List B

Ingredients: 2 lbs. spareribs, cut into 4 equal servings
1 lemon, sliced
1 onion, sliced
½ cup catsup
1 tbsp. Worcestershire sauce (or to taste)
1 tsp. chili powder
1 tsp. salt
2 dashes Tabasco sauce
2 cups water

Method: 1. Place ribs in shallow baking pan; top with lemon and onion slices; secure with toothpicks.
2. Bake in hot oven (450°F) for ½ hour.
3. Combine remaining ingredients and heat to boiling point; pour over spareribs; reduce oven temperature to 350°F.
4. Bake for 1 hour, basting every 15 minutes.

FRANK-PINEAPPLE KABOBS

Yield: 4 kabobs or 4 servings

Exchange 1 serving for: 1 Meat Exchange
and 2 Fat Exchanges
and ½ Fruit Exchange

Ingredients: 4 wieners
4 slices bacon
1 small green pepper
one 8-oz. tin pineapple tidbits, unsweetened
4 tsps. salad oil
1 tsp. Worcestershire sauce

Method: 1. Cut each wiener into 3 pieces and bacon into squares.
2. Cut green pepper into 12 pieces.
3. Alternate pieces of wiener, green pepper, bacon and pineapple tidbits on four skewers.
4. Mix juice from pineapple with salad oil and Worcestershire sauce and brush over kabobs.
5. Broil on barbecue for 7 to 12 minutes, turning often.

VEAL SCALLOPINI

Yield: 4 servings

Exchange 1 serving for: 3 Meat Exchanges
and 1 Vegetable Exchange List 2A

Ingredients: 1 lb. stewing veal, cut in 2″ cubes
½ cup thinly sliced onions
½ cup thinly sliced carrots
1 lb. thinly sliced mushrooms
¼ tsp. paprika
1¼ cups water
2 tsps. shortening or margarine
salt and pepper
juice of 1 lemon

Method: 1. Pan-fry diced veal in shortening or margarine.
2. Add vegetables, seasonings and water; simmer until tender.
3. Add more water gradually as liquid simmers down.
4. Just before serving, add lemon juice.
5. Serve with cooked noodles.

Note: Allow ⅓ cup cooked noodles for 1 Bread Exchange.

BARBECUED CHICKEN

Yield: 4 servings

Exchange 1 serving for: 3 Meat Exchanges
and 1 Calorie Poor Food List B

Ingredients: one 2 lb. frying chicken
¼ cup vinegar
½ cup catsup
dash of Tabasco sauce
1 cup water

Method: 1. Cut chicken into 4 servings and place in a baking pan, skin side down.
2. Mix other ingredients and pour over chicken.
3. Bake in moderate oven (350°F) for ½ hour.
4. Turn chicken over, baste with sauce and continue baking for another ½ hour.

BRAISED VEAL WITH HERBS

Yield: 4 servings

Exchange 1 serving for: 3 Meat Exchanges
and 1 Fat Exchange
and 1 Vegetable Exchange List 2B

Ingredients: 1 lb. veal cutlet
4 tsps. cooking oil
1 medium onion, cut into rings
1 clove garlic (optional)
¼ cup water
1 tbsp. lemon juice
1 tsp. salt
¼ tsp. crushed oregano
1 tbsp. chopped parsley

Method: 1. Cut veal into 4 servings.
2. Heat oil in large skillet; add veal; cook until brown on both sides; remove from pan.
3. Add onions and garlic; cook until onions are tender; remove garlic.
4. Add veal, water, lemon juice, salt and oregano; cover and simmer over low heat, turning meat occasionally until tender (about 30 minutes); add additional water if needed.
5. Serve with chopped parsley.

CURRIED LAMB

Yield: 4 servings

Exchange 1 serving for: 2 Meat Exchanges
and 1 Fat Exchange
and 1 Bread Exchange
and 1 Vegetable Exchange List 2B

Ingredients: ½ cup chopped celery
⅓ cup onions
4 tsps. cooking oil
1 cup or 8 oz. cooked diced lamb
1⅓ cups beef broth
2 drops Tabasco sauce
⅛ tsp. curry powder
½ tsp. salt
1⅓ cups cooked rice

Method: 1. Brown celery and onion in oil.
2. Add broth, meat and spices; stir over low heat until well mixed and hot; if it becomes too dry add more broth.
3. Pour meat mixture over rice to serve.

OVEN BAKED CHICKEN

Yield: 4 servings

Exchange 1 serving for: 3 Meat Exchanges
and 1 Fat Exchange
and 1 Bread Exchange

Ingredients: one 2 lb. frying chicken cut into 4 servings
¾ to 1 cup cornflake crumbs
2 tbsps. cooking oil

Method: 1. Remove skin and fat from chicken parts; rinse chicken and dry thoroughly.
2. Place chicken on large plate and drizzle oil over it; make sure each piece is coated.
3. Spread cornflake crumbs on a large piece of waxed paper.
4. Coat each piece of chicken well with crumbs; let stand briefly so that coating will stick.
5. Heat oven to 425°F; line large, flat baking pan with foil and oil lightly; warm the pan and place the chicken parts on it so they do not touch.
6. Bake in hot oven for 45 minutes or until tender.

LEMON BROILED CHICKEN

Yield: 4 servings

Exchange 1 serving for: 3 Meat Exchanges
and 1 Fat Exchange

Ingredients: one 2 lb. frying chicken
¼ cup lemon juice
⅛ cup melted butter or margarine
1 small onion, grated
1 clove garlic, minced
½ tsp. salt
½ tsp. celery salt
½ tsp. black pepper
½ tsp. rosemary
¼ tsp. thyme

Method: 1. Cut chicken into 4 servings and marinate in barbecue mixture (made by combining remaining ingredients) for several hours.

2. Broil chicken pieces, turning and brushing often with marinade, until done.

KABOB OF CHICKEN LIVERS

Yield: 4 kabobs or 4 servings

Exchange 1 kabob for: 3 Meat Exchanges
and 1 Fat Exchange
and 1 Calorie Poor Food List B

Ingredients: 1 lb. chicken livers
½ lb. mushroom caps
4 tsps. butter or margarine
salt, pepper, onion salt

Method: 1. Alternate chicken livers and mushroom caps on 4 skewers, dividing evenly.

2. Brush lightly with butter or margarine.

3. Broil 3" from broiler for 10 minutes, turning often; season to taste.

BAKED HALIBUT ROYALE

Yield: 4 servings

Exchange 1 serving for: 3 Meat Exchanges
and 1 Vegetable Exchange List 2B
and 1 Fat Exchange

Ingredients: 1 lb. boneless halibut steak, cut into 4 equal servings
½ tsp. salt
¼ tsp. paprika
pinch of cayenne pepper
juice of 1 lemon
¼ cup chopped onion
4 tsps. butter or margarine
thin green pepper strips

Method: 1. Sprinkle steaks with seasonings and lemon juice.

2. Marinate in refrigerator for 1 hour, turning once.

3. Sauté onion in butter.

4. Place steaks in a greased baking dish and spread with sautéed onion.

5. Top with green pepper strips.

6. Bake in hot oven (450°F to 500°F) for 10 minutes.

FILLETS IN LEMON BUTTER SAUCE

Yield: 4 servings

Exchange 1 serving for: 3 Meat Exchanges
and 1 Fat Exchange

Ingredients: 1 lb. boneless fish fillets, cut into 4 equal servings
1 tbsp. lemon juice
1 tbsp. finely chopped parsley
4 tsps. melted butter or margarine
¼ tsp. salt
⅛ tsp. pepper

Method: 1. Arrange fillets in a greased baking dish.

2. Combine remaining ingredients and pour over fillets.

3. Bake in a hot oven (450°F to 500°F) for 8 minutes (fresh fish) or 15 minutes (frozen fish).

BAKED FISH FILLETS

Yield: 4 servings

Exchange 1 serving for: 3 Meat Exchanges
and ½ Bread Exchange
and 1 Fat Exchange

Ingredients: 1 lb. boneless fish fillets
¼ cup milk
½ tsp. salt
4 tbsps. fine dry bread crumbs
4 tsps. butter or other fat

Method: 1. Cut fillets into four portions and soak 3 minutes in milk, to which salt has been added.

2. Drain and roll in bread crumbs.

3. Place fish on greased baking dish and dot with fat.

4. Bake in hot oven (450°F to 500°F) for 8 minutes (fresh fish) and 15 minutes (frozen fish).

BAKED FISH IN CATSUP SAUCE

Yield: 4 servings

Exchange 1 serving for: 3 Meat Exchanges
and 1 Vegetable Exchange List 2A

Ingredients: 1 lb. boneless fish fillets cut into 4 equal servings
⅔ cup chopped onion
1 tsp. butter or other fat
2 tsps. flour
1 bouillon cube, dissolved in ½ cup hot water
4 tbsps. catsup
½ cup sliced dill pickle

Method: 1. Place fish in greased baking dish.

2. Cook onion in fat in a saucepan; stir in flour.

3. Gradually add bouillon mixture and catsup; cook, stirring constantly until blended.

4. Simmer uncovered for 10 minutes; add dill pickles.

5. Pour sauce over fish.

6. Bake in a hot oven (450°F to 500°F) for 15 minutes (fresh fish) or 25 minutes (frozen fish).

BAKED FINNAN HADDIE

Yield: 4 servings

Exchange 1 serving for: 3 Meat Exchanges
and 1 Fat Exchange
and ½ Milk Exchange

Ingredients: 1 lb. finnan haddie (smoked fillets of haddock)
1 cup milk
4 tsps. butter or margarine
paprika

Method: 1. Cut fish into 4 equal servings; place in greased baking dish; add milk; dot with butter and sprinkle with paprika.
2. Bake in slow oven (325°F) for ½ hour.

BAKED SALMON

Yield: 8 servings

Exchange 1 serving for: 3 Meat Exchanges
and 1 Vegetable Exchange List 2B

Ingredients: 1 cup water
½ cup chopped onion
¼ cup lemon juice
½ tsp. salt
½ tsp. pepper
2 lemon slices
2 lbs. salmon steaks cut into 8 equal servings
2 tbsps. flour

Method: 1. Combine water, onion, lemon juice, salt and pepper and lemon slices in saucepan; simmer for 20 minutes.
2. Wash and dry salmon steaks; place in centre of sheet of foil on baking pan.
3. Pour the sauce mixture over fish; seal foil carefully.
4. Bake at 375°F for 30 to 45 minutes or until the fish flakes easily with a fork.
5. Remove fish to a platter and pour remaining juices into a saucepan; add flour to juices and cook over medium heat until thickened; pour over fish and serve.

FISH FILLETS IN MUSHROOM SAUCE

Yield: 4 servings

Exchange 1 serving for: 3 Meat Exchanges
and 2 Fat Exchanges
and ½ Bread Exchange
and 1 Milk Exchange

54

Ingredients: 1 cup fresh mushrooms
3 tbsps. butter or margarine
2½ tbsps. flour
½ tsp. salt
dash of cayenne pepper
2 cups skim milk
1 lb. boneless fish fillets cut into 4 equal servings
½ tsp. salt
¼ cup soft bread crumbs

Method: 1. Wash and slice mushrooms.
2. Sauté in butter for 5 minutes.
3. Add flour and seasonings, mixing to a smooth paste.
4. Add milk gradually, stirring constantly; cook until thickened.
5. Place fillets in baking dish and sprinkle with salt.
6. Cover with sauce; top with bread crumbs; bake in moderate oven (375°F) for ½ hour.

VEGETABLE-STUFFED FILLET ROLLS

Yield: 6 rolls or 3 servings

Exchange 2 rolls for: 3 Meat Exchanges
and 1 Vegetable Exchange List 2B

Ingredients: 1 lb. thin fish fillets (sole is especially good)
¼ tsp. salt
⅛ tsp. pepper
Vegetable Stuffing:
1 tsp. melted butter or other fat
½ tbsp. lemon juice
⅛ cup chopped onion
½ cup chopped tomato
½ cup chopped cucumber

Method: 1. Skin fillets and slice into 6 strips 6" by 12".
2. Season fillets on both sides.
3. Line greased muffin tins or custard cups with fillets.
4. Mix stuffing ingredients together; season and divide evenly into fillet rings.
5. Combine melted fat and lemon juice and pour over rolls.
6. Bake in a hot oven (450°F to 500°F) for 15 minutes.

SAUCES AND ACCOMPANIMENTS
SEASONING SALT

Ingredients: 2 tbsps. salt

2 tbsps. paprika

1 tsp. onion salt

1 tsp. black pepper

1½ tsps. monosodium glutamate

1 tsp. celery salt

1 tsp. garlic salt

Method: 1. Mix well.

2. Store in tightly capped jar.

CRANBERRY SAUCE

Yield: Approximately 2 cups

Exchange 1 tbsp. for: 1 Calorie Poor Food List B.

Ingredients: 2 cups raw cranberries

⅓ cup water

1 tsp. artificial liquid sweetener

Method: 1. Cook cranberries in water until berries pop and soften.

2. Add artificial liquid sweetener; chill.

CAPER SAUCE

Yield: ½ cup or 4 servings

Exchange 2 tbsps. for: 2 Fat Exchanges

and 1 Calorie Poor Food List B

Ingredients: 3 tbsps. melted butter or margarine

juice of 1 lemon

1 tbsp. chopped parsley

1 tbsp. minced capers

freshly ground black pepper

salt

Method: 1. Combine ingredients; store in refrigerator.

ORANGE CRANBERRY RELISH

Yield: Approximately 2 cups

Exchange 1 tbsp. for: 1 Calorie Poor Food List B

Ingredients: ½ lb. raw cranberries

1½ oranges

lemon juice

artificial liquid sweetener to taste

Method: 1. Wash cranberries.

2. Wash and quarter unpeeled oranges.

3. Put oranges and cranberries through food chopper.

4. Add lemon juice and artificial liquid sweetener; mix well.

5. Store in refrigerator for several hours to blend flavours.

MINT SAUCE

Yield: ½ cup
Exchange 1 serving for: 1 Calorie Free Food List A
Ingredients: ¼ cup vinegar
¼ cup water
4 tbsps. chopped fresh mint (dried, if fresh not available)
⅓ tsp. artificial liquid sweetener
Method: 1. Heat vinegar and water to boiling point.
2. Pour over mint and artificial liquid sweetener.
3. Let steep; store in tightly covered jar in refrigerator.

HOT BARBECUE SAUCE

Yield: 1⅓ cups or 4 servings
Exchange 1 serving for: 1 Calorie Free Food List A
Ingredients: ½ cup lemon juice
⅓ cup cider vinegar
¼ cup tomato juice
¼ cup cold water
1 tsp. salt
1 tsp. dry mustard
1 tsp. paprika
⅓ tsp. artificial liquid sweetener
½ tsp. pepper
½ tsp. red pepper
½ tsp. onion powder
1 tsp. Tabasco sauce
1 tsp. butter or margarine
⅛ tsp. garlic powder
Method: 1. Combine ingredients in saucepan and heat to boiling point.
2. Store in refrigerator.

CUCUMBER SAUCE

Yield: 1 cup
Exchange 1 tbsp. for: 1 Fat Exchange
Ingredients: ½ cup whipped cream
2 tbsps. vinegar or lemon juice
¼ tsp. salt
white pepper to taste
½ cup chopped cucumber
1 tsp. chopped pimento
Method: 1. Drain chopped cucumber.
2. Beat vinegar slowly into whipped cream and add seasonings.
3. Fold in cucumber and pimento.
4. Store in refrigerator.

TARTAR SAUCE

Yield: 1 cup

Exchange 1 tbsp. for: 1 Fat Exchange

Ingredients: 1 cup commercial mayonnaise
½ tbsp. chopped olives
½ tbsp. chopped pickles, drained
½ tbsp. capers
½ tbsp. chopped parsley
½ tbsp. onion juice

Method: 1. Combine all ingredients and mix well.
2. Store in refrigerator.

TOMATO SAUCE

Yield: 2 cups

Exchange 2 tbsps. for: 1 Vegetable Exchange List 2B

Ingredients: 1 tbsp. butter or margarine
1 tbsp. finely chopped onion
5 tbsps. flour
2 cups canned tomatoes
1½ tsps. salt
⅓ tsp. artificial liquid sweetener
¼ tsp. pepper
½ tsp. celery salt

Method: 1. Sauté onion in butter; add flour; mix well.
2. Add tomatoes and seasonings; cook, stirring constantly until thick; serve hot.
3. Store in refrigerator.

HOT MUSTARD

Yield: Approximately ¾ cup

Exchange 1 tsp. for: 1 Calorie Poor Food List B

Ingredients: 3 tbsps. dry mustard
⅓ tsp. artificial liquid sweetener
1 egg, beaten
¼ cup vinegar
¼ cup water

Method: 1. Mix mustard, artificial liquid sweetener, and beaten egg.
2. Add water and vinegar gradually.
3. Cook in double boiler over hot water, stirring constantly until thick; chill and store in refrigerator.

LEMON SAUCE

Yield: Approximately ½ cup
Exchange 1½ tbsps. for: 1 Fat Exchange
Ingredients: 2 tbsps. lemon juice
                3 tbsps. finely chopped parsley
                4 tbsps. corn oil
                1 tsp. salt
                ¼ tsp. pepper
                1¼ tsps. dry mustard
                1¼ tsps. Worcestershire sauce
Method: 1. Combine all ingredients.
           2. Store in refrigerator.

STUFFING FOR FOWL

Yield: 1 serving
Exchange for: 1 Bread Exchange
              and 1 Fat Exchange
Ingredients: 1 slice bread
                ½ tsp. chopped onion
                pinch of salt
                f.g. pepper
                ⅛ tsp. poultry seasoning
                1 tsp. butter or margarine
                water to moisten
Method: 1. Crumble or cut the bread into small cubes.
           2. Add onion, salt, pepper, poultry seasoning and melted butter or margarine; mix well.
           3. Add sufficient water to moisten.
Variation: A good stuffing may be made without butter or margarine, in which case the exchange would be only 1 Bread Exchange.

STUFFING FOR WHOLE TURKEY

Yield: Sufficient stuffing for one turkey 10 to 15 lbs.
Exchange ½ cup for: 1 Bread Exchange
                  and 1 Fat Exchange
Ingredients: 1½ loaves bread (about 34 slices)
                2 onions, chopped
                2 tsps. salt
                pepper to taste
                1 to 2 tsps. poultry seasoning
                5 tbsps. + 2 tsps. melted butter or margarine
                water to moisten
Method: Proceed as for individual amount of stuffing.

STUFFING FOR FISH

Yield: 4 servings

Exchange 1 serving for: 1 Bread Exchange
and 1 Fat Exchange

Ingredients: 4 slices bread, cubed or crumbled
2 tsps. chopped onion
2 tsps. green pickle relish
4 tsps. melted butter or margarine
water to moisten

Method: Combine all ingredients.

YORKSHIRE PUDDING

Yield: 12 individual portions

Exchange 1 portion for: 1 Fat Exchange
and ½ Bread Exchange

Ingredients: 3 tbsps. hot water
1 beef bouillon cube
5 tbsps. oil
1 cup sifted all purpose flour
½ tsp. salt
1 cup skim milk
4 egg whites, beaten stiff

Method: 1. Preheat oven to 425°F.
2. Dissolve beef bouillon cube in hot water; boil if necessary.
3. Add 3 tbsps. oil; boil until water is gone.
4. Put ½ tsp. of this mixture into each of 12 deep muffin cups; place in oven to keep hot until ready to be filled.
5. Add remaining liquid ingredients to dry ingredients.
6. Beat with electric beater for 30 seconds or until mixture is smooth; fold in egg whites.
7. Divide mixture evenly into 12 muffin cups.
8. Bake for 15 minutes; reduce to 375°F; bake for 30 minutes.
9. Cut small slit in side of each after removing from oven; serve immediately.

CASSEROLES

Every homemaker dreams of creating memorable dishes from leftovers. A casserole dish is the answer to her dream — and here we offer a collection of recipe ideas so that diabetics and their families may enjoy the subtle blend of flavours and the economy that such dishes afford. Casseroles are helpful too, in preparing meals for the family ahead of time, ready to be served whenever they are needed.

In these recipes, designed with the diabetic in mind, raw minced meat may be replaced with cooked minced or diced meat. Except for ingredients such as eggs or bread crumbs, used as thickening agents, the amounts of the ingredients — meat, vegetables, etc. — may be increased or decreased to suit the amounts allowed in the meal plan of the diabetic.

The recipes are given for family amounts, and any suitable casserole dish may be used for cooking or baking. Individual casseroles are attractive too, and if care is taken in dividing the mixture, the recipe may be baked and served in individual dishes. When baking, place the oven rack so that the top of the product is at the centre of the oven, and place the casserole so it is as near the centre of the oven as possible, for efficient circulation of heat.

MACARONI AND CHEESE #1

Yield: 4 servings

Exchange 1 serving for: 1 Bread Exchange
and 2 Meat Exchanges
and 1 Vegetable Exchange List 2B

Ingredients: 2 cups cooked macaroni
2 cups grated cheese
1⅓ cups tomato juice
salt and pepper to taste

Method: 1. Place cooked macaroni in casserole dish; add tomato juice and seasonings to taste.

2. Sprinkle grated cheese over the mixture and place under broiler or bake in moderate oven (350°F) until cheese is bubbly and browned.

Note: Canned tomatoes may be used in place of tomato juice.

MACARONI AND CHEESE #2

Yield: 4 servings

Exchange 1 serving for: 2 Meat Exchanges
and 1 Milk Exchange
and 1 Bread Exchange

Ingredients: 2 cups macaroni, cooked, drained and rinsed in cold water
8 oz. or 2 cups grated cheese
¼ tsp. dry mustard
1 tsp. grated onion (optional)
2 cups whole milk
½ tsp. salt
f.g. pepper

Method: 1. Cover bottom of a lightly greased casserole dish with half the cooked macaroni and sprinkle 1 cup cheese over macaroni.

2. Add 1 cup milk, to which seasonings and onions have been added.

3. Add remaining macaroni and milk; top with remaining grated cheese.

4. Bake 30 minutes at 325°F.

CHEESE SOUFFLE

Yield: 4 servings

Exchange 1 serving for: 2 Meat Exchanges
and 1 Vegetable Exchange List 2A

Ingredients: 4 tbsps. flour
⅓ cup 2% milk, cold
½ cup 2% milk, heated
⅛ tsp. salt
4 egg yolks
4 egg whites, stiffly beaten
3 oz. (or ¾ cup) grated cheddar cheese

Method:
1. Mix flour and cold milk together to form paste.
2. Add heated milk and egg yolks, and cook in top of double boiler until thick, stirring frequently.
3. Remove from heat.
4. Fold in cheese and egg whites.
5. Bake in casserole dish at 300°F for 1 hour.

Variations: In place of ¾ cup grated cheese, ¾ cup minced cooked chicken or ham or ¾ cup drained flaked fish may be used (tuna or salmon).

SHEPHERD'S PIE

Yield: 4 servings

Exchange 1 serving for: 2 Meat Exchanges
and 1 Bread Exchange

Ingredients: 2 cups minced cooked beef
salt and pepper to taste
1 tbsp. plus 1 tsp. grated onion
1⅓ cups mashed potato
clear fat free broth or consommé

Method:
1. Add seasonings and onion to minced cooked beef; mix well.
2. Add broth or consommé to moisten.
3. Place in a casserole dish.
4. Spread mashed potato over the top.
5. Place in moderate oven (350°F-375°F) until heated through and potatoes are slightly browned.

Note: If the Meat Exchange is three for this meal rather than two, use ¾ cup minced cooked beef per serving.

Variations:
1. Pipe potato around edge of casserole dish and garnish with 1 tsp. catsup per serving.
   Increase food value by 1 Calorie Poor Food List B.
2. Substitute green pepper (1 tbsp. per serving) for onion.

WIENERS AND BEANS

Yield: 4 servings

Exchange 1 serving for: 2 Meat Exchanges
and 1 Vegetable Exchange List 2A

Ingredients: 1 cup cooked navy beans
½ cup tomato juice
seasonings to taste
8 wieners

Method: 1. Place beans in casserole; add heated tomato juice and seasonings.
2. Arrange wieners on top of casserole.
3. Place in oven and bake at 350°F for 15 to 20 minutes, or until wieners are slightly brown and tomato juice is bubbling.

BAKED WIENERS CREOLE

Yield: 4 servings

Exchange 1 serving for: 2 Meat Exchanges
and 1 Vegetable Exchange List 2A
and 1 Calorie Poor Food List B

Ingredients: 3 cups canned tomatoes
2 whole cloves
½ clove garlic
1 bay leaf
¼ cup chopped green pepper
¼ cup chopped celery
salt and pepper to taste
8 wieners

Method: 1. Combine tomatoes, garlic, cloves and bay leaf.
2. Simmer uncovered ¾ hour.
3. Add green pepper and celery and simmer an additional 15 minutes.
4. Remove bay leaf and cloves.
5. Place wieners in casserole; pour sauce over top.
6. Bake uncovered at 350°F for 15 minutes.

Variation: Cut wieners in 1″ pieces and heat in sauce on top of stove.

CHILI CON CARNE

Yield: 4 servings

Exchange 1 serving for: 2 Meat Exchanges
and 1 Bread Exchange
and 1 Vegetable Exchange List 2A

Ingredients: 1½ cups (1 lb.) raw lean minced beef
2 tbsps. chopped onion
3 cups canned tomatoes
2 drops Tabasco sauce
¼ tsp. chili powder
½ tsp. salt
1⅓ cups canned kidney beans

Method: 1. Brown minced beef over medium heat, preferably in 2-quart "top-of-range" casserole dish, stirring to separate the meat.
2. Add onion, canned tomatoes, Tabasco sauce, chili powder and salt.
3. Cover and simmer 1 hour, stirring occasionally.
4. Add kidney beans and reheat before serving.

SAUSAGE-APPLE-ONION BAKE

Yield: 4 servings
Exchange 1 serving for: 3 Meat Exchanges
and 1 Vegetable Exchange List 2A
and 1 Fruit Exchange
and 1 Calorie Poor Food List B

Ingredients: 4 medium-sized onions
1 tsp. salt
¼ tsp. monosodium glutamate
2¼ cups (1½ lbs.) sausage meat
2 medium, tart apples
1 tsp. salt
½ tsp. nutmeg
½ tsp. artificial liquid sweetener
2 tbsps. unsweetened orange juice

Method: 1. Cut onions in ¼" slices; cover with boiling water; add salt and monosodium glutamate; boil 5 minutes; drain.
2. Shape sausage meat into 8 patties and pan broil until browned.
3. Wash and core apples and cut into ¼" cross-wise slices; mix with cooked onions, and arrange in bottom of a 2 quart casserole dish.
4. Mix salt, nutmeg, artificial liquid sweetener, and orange juice; drizzle over the apple mixture and arrange browned sausage patties on top (2 per serving).
5. Cover tightly and bake at 350°F for 25 minutes; uncover and bake 15 to 20 minutes or until apples are tender.

GROUND BEEF CASSEROLE

Yield: 4 servings

Exchange 1 serving for: 2 Meat Exchanges
and 1 Vegetable Exchange List 2B

Ingredients: 1½ cups (1 lb.) raw minced beef
¼ cup green pepper, chopped or sliced
1 tbsp. chopped onion
salt and pepper to taste
1⅓ cups canned tomatoes

Method: 1. Brown minced beef over high heat, stirring to separate it.
2. Place half the meat in bottom of a one-quart casserole.
3. Place half the onion and green pepper on top.
4. Season, and add half the tomatoes.
5. Add the remainder of the minced beef, onions and green pepper, and pour the remaining tomatoes over the mixture.
6. Bake ½ to ¾ hour at 350°F.

Suggestions for serving:
1. Serve with ⅓ cup cooked rice, spaghetti or noodles and add 1 Bread Exchange.
2. Use cooked minced beef or ham in place of the raw beef.
3. Fresh tomatoes may be used, sliced in layers between the meat. Use four medium-sized tomatoes in place of 1⅓ cups canned tomatoes.

BEEF SPAGHETTI CREOLE

Yield: 4 servings

Exchange 1 serving for: 2 Meat Exchanges
and 1 Vegetable Exchange List 2B
and 1 Bread Exchange

Ingredients: 1½ cups (1 lb.) lean raw minced beef
2 tbsps. finely chopped onion
2 tbsps. chopped green pepper
2 tbsps. sliced mushrooms
1⅓ cups canned tomatoes
salt and pepper to taste
dash of oregano and thyme
1 bay leaf
1⅓ cups cooked spaghetti

Method: 1. Brown minced beef; drain off excess fat.
2. Add onion, green pepper, mushrooms, canned tomatoes and seasonings.
3. Simmer 30 minutes; remove bay leaf.
4. Serve over the spaghetti which has been kept warm over boiling water. Allow ⅓ cup cooked spaghetti per serving.

HUNGARIAN GOULASH

Yield: 4 servings

Exchange 1 serving for: 3 Meat Exchanges
and 1 Vegetable Exchange List 2B
and 1 Fat Exchange

Ingredients: 1 lb. round steak cut in ¾″ cubes
½ cup chopped onion
1 clove garlic, minced
1 tsp. paprika
½ tsp. salt
dash of pepper and thyme
1 bay leaf
⅔ cup canned tomatoes
3 tbsps. canned tomato paste
½ cup commercial sour cream

Method: 1. Sear meat in frying pan.
2. Reduce heat; add onion, garlic and seasonings.
3. Blend canned tomatoes and tomato paste with the meat mixture.
4. Simmer, stirring occasionally until the meat is tender (about 1 hour).
5. If liquid cooks down too much during simmering add water to bring to desired consistency.
6. Remove from heat and blend in sour cream.
7. Serve hot on cooked broad noodles, if desired.
Exchange ⅓ cup of cooked broad noodles for: 1 Bread Exchange.

CORNED BEEF HASH

Yield: 4 servings

Exchange 1 serving for: 3 Meat Exchanges
and I Bread Exchange
and 1 Vegetable Exchange List 2A

Ingredients: 1½ cups crumbled canned corned beef
2 cups diced, cooked potatoes
2 tsps. minced onion
⅔ cup tomato sauce
½ cup beef broth, fat removed
salt and pepper to taste
4 poached eggs

Method: 1. Brown corned beef, onions, and potatoes in hot frying pan.
2. Mix tomato sauce with broth and combine with meat mixture.
3. Season and heat thoroughly.
4. Serve one poached egg on top of each serving of hash.

BEEF STROGANOFF

Yield: 4 servings

Exchange 1 serving for: 2 Meat Exchanges
and 1 Vegetable Exchange List 2A

Ingredients: 10 oz. ground lean beef
1 cup sliced mushrooms
4 tsps. chopped onion and green pepper mixed
¾ cup undiluted canned condensed cream of mushroom soup
¾ cup water
1 tsp. salt

Method: 1. Brown meat slowly in frying pan.
2. Add mushrooms, onion and green pepper and continue cooking for 2 or 3 minutes.
3. Add soup, water and salt; mix thoroughly with meat and vegetables.
4. Simmer slowly until meat is cooked (about 20 minutes).
5. Serve hot over cooked broad noodles or rice, if desired. Exchange ⅓ cup broad noodles or rice for: 1 Bread Exchange.

BEEF CASSEROLE

Yield: 6 servings

Exchange 1 serving for: 3 Meat Exchanges
and 1 Bread Exchange
and 1 Fat Exchange

Ingredients: 1½ lbs. round steak
2 tbsps. fat
6 medium onions
3 cups hot water
1 bay leaf
2½ cups diced carrots
1½ cups raw green beans (cut in strips)
salt and pepper to taste

Method:
1. Wipe meat with a clean damp cloth and cut into 1″ pieces.
2. Melt fat in casserole dish over medium heat; add meat, and brown slowly on all sides.
3. During browning of meat, add 2 of the onions which have been thinly sliced; finish browning the meat.
4. Slowly add hot water and 1 bay leaf; cover casserole dish and simmer 1½ hours.
5. If necessary, add more water as meat cooks.
6. Add the 4 remaining onions, quartered, and carrots and beans.
7. Cover casserole dish and place in 350°F oven; bake ¾ hour or until vegetables are tender.
8. Remove bay leaf before serving.

SALMON AND CELERY CASSEROLE

Yield: 4 servings

Exchange 1 serving for: 1 Meat Exchange
and 1 Vegetable Exchange List 2A

Ingredients: 1 cup canned salmon
¾ cup canned condensed cream of celery soup, undiluted
salt and pepper to taste

Method:
1. Combine ingredients.
2. Place in a casserole dish.
3. Bake in moderate oven (325°F to 350°F) until browned.

Note: ¼ cup to ½ cup water may be used to dilute the soup, if desired, before mixing with the salmon.

SALMON CASSEROLE

Yield: 4 servings

Exchange 1 serving for: 2 Meat Exchanges
and 1 Milk Exchange
and 1 Calorie Poor Food List B

Ingredients: 4 medium sized eggs
2 cups whole milk
salt and pepper to taste
1 cup flaked, cooked or canned salmon
½ medium onion, grated

Method: 1. Beat egg; add milk, salt and pepper, and mix well.
2. Mix grated onion with the salmon.
3. Add salmon to the milk and egg mixture, and mix well.
4. Pour into a one-quart casserole dish or into four individual casserole dishes.
5. Place casserole in shallow pan containing 1″ of hot water.
6. Bake at 300°F-325°F until set (about ¾ hour).

TUNA FISH CASSEROLE

Yield: 4 servings

Exchange 1 serving for: 2 Meat Exchanges
and 1 Bread Exchange
and 1 Fat Exchange

Ingredients: 2 cups canned flaked tuna fish
¾ cup canned condensed cream of mushroom soup, undiluted
¾ cup cooked, drained rice or noodles
2 tsps. lemon juice
salt and pepper to taste
water
4 tsps. butter or margarine or 12 sliced ripe olives

Method: 1. Mix first 5 ingredients together.
2. Add water to moisten (⅓-½ cup).
3. Place mixture in a casserole dish and bake in moderate oven (325°F-350°F) until it bubbles.
4. Dot top of casserole with butter or margarine, or mix ripe olives with other ingredients; serve hot.

Variations: 1. In place of 2 cups tuna fish, 2 cups flaked canned salmon, crab meat, lobster or shrimp may be used.
2. If butter or olives are not used, subtract 1 Fat Exchange.

CHICKEN and RICE or NOODLE CASSEROLE

Yield: 4 servings

Exchange 1 serving for: 2 Meat Exchanges
and 1 Bread Exchange

Ingredients: 2 cups diced cooked chicken
1⅓ cups cooked drained rice or noodles
1 cup clear chicken broth
salt and pepper to taste

Method: 1. Combine all ingredients; place in one-quart casserole, or, if desired, divide evenly into four individual casseroles.
2. Bake in moderate oven (350°F) until bubbling hot.

Variations: 1. Add chopped parsley and mushrooms from Calorie Free Food List A. No change in the Exchange Value of the recipe.
2. Mix ½-1 tsp. curry with the broth before you add it to the other ingredients. No change in the Exchange value of the recipe.
3. Add 2 rounded tbsps. chopped celery, green pepper, pimento or onion from Calorie Poor Food List B. To Exchange Value add 1 Calorie Poor Food List B.

CHICKEN SUPREME

Yield: 4 servings

Exchange 1 serving for: 2 Meat Exchanges
and 1 Vegetable Exchange List 2A

Ingredients: ¾ cup chicken broth, with fat removed
½ cup canned condensed cream of mushroom soup, undiluted
⅛ tsp. pepper
½ cup frozen peas
4 tsps. chopped pimento
2 cups cooked, diced chicken

Method: 1. Mix broth, soup and pepper.
2. Add remaining ingredients.
3. Pour into 1-quart casserole.
4. Bake at 325°F for 30 to 40 minutes.

CHICKEN A LA KING

Yield: 4 servings

Exchange 1 serving (without toast) for: 3 Meat Exchanges
and 1 Bread Exchange

Ingredients: 8 mushrooms, sliced
½ cup clear chicken broth
2 cups skim milk
¼ cup flour
½ tsp. salt
dash of pepper
1 tbsp. chopped pimento
3 cups diced cooked chicken

Method:
1. Cook mushrooms in broth.
2. Drain and measure broth; add water to make ½ cup.
3. Heat 1½ cups milk and ½ cup broth in double boiler.
4. Blend flour and the remaining ½ cup skim milk until no lumps remain.
5. Add to heated milk and broth, stirring constantly until thickened, over the boiling water.
6. Add chicken, mushrooms, pimento and seasonings; reheat.
7. Serve in individual casserole dishes or on toast. (Add necessary Bread Exchange if toast is used.)

Note: If whole milk is used, the exchange per serving is increased by 1 Fat Exchange.

CHICKEN FRICASSEE

Yield: 4 servings

Exchange 1 serving for: 2 Meat Exchanges
and 1 Vegetable Exchange List 2A

Ingredients: 1 cup chicken broth from which the fat is removed
½ cup diced raw carrots
½ cup chopped celery
3 tbsps. chopped onion
2 tsps. chopped pimento
2 cups (8 oz.) cooked chicken pieces, bones and skin removed
salt and pepper to taste

Method:
1. Heat broth in saucepan; add carrots, celery and onion; simmer for about 10 minutes.
2. Add chicken, pimento and seasonings and continue to simmer until vegetables are tender; serve hot.

CHOP SUEY

Yield: 4 servings

Exchange 1 serving for: 3 Meat Exchanges
and 1 Vegetable Exchange List 2A

Ingredients: ½ cup chopped green pepper
1 cup diagonally cut celery
½ cup sliced onion
1 cup chicken or beef broth with fat removed
2 cups cooked, diced chicken or beef
1 cup drained canned bean sprouts
2 tbsps. flour
2 tbsps. soy sauce
½ cup small or sliced mushrooms

Method: 1. Cook pepper, celery and onion slowly in ½ cup broth.
2. Add chicken or beef and bean sprouts.
3. Combine flour with remaining broth and blend until smooth; add gradually to meat mixture, stirring until thickened and cooked.
4. Add soy sauce and mushrooms and heat thoroughly; serve on rice.

Note: If rice is used, allow ⅓ cup cooked rice for: 1 Bread Exchange.

PORK CHOW MEIN

Yield: 4 servings

Exchange 1 serving for: 3 Meat Exchanges
and 1 Vegetable Exchange List 2B
and 1 Vegetable Exchange List 2A

Ingredients: 1 lb. lean raw pork cut in thin strips
1 cup diagonally cut celery
1⅓ cups sliced onion
1 cup sliced canned, drained mushrooms
1 tsp. cornstarch
1 can consommé (10 oz.)
¼ cup soy sauce
2 cups canned drained bean sprouts

Method: 1. Brown pork strips in frying pan.
2. Add celery, onion and mushrooms; cook until tender crisp.
3. Blend consommé, soy sauce and cornstarch and stir into mixture; add bean sprouts; heat thoroughly.

Note: If Chow Mein is served on rice allow ⅓ cup cooked rice for: 1 Bread Exchange.
If, instead of rice, Chow Mein noodles are placed on top of each serving, allow ½ cup Chow Mein noodles per serving and exchange for: 1 Bread Exchange and 1 Fat Exchange.

SALADS

Salads are often the bright spots in our meals. With their crisp green and colourful vegetables and fruits, they can tempt the dullest appetite. For diabetics, they are especially important, since they provide essential roughage, minerals, and vitamins in addition to the necessary measured amounts of other nutrients. Some salads serve as appetizers or main course accompaniments. Others are heartier and may take the place of the main dish at luncheon or supper. Whatever their role in the menu plan, salads should be fresh, simple, colourful and attractive and should taste good! The salad planned for the diabetic can represent a Vegetable Exchange, a Fruit Exchange, a Meat Exchange, a Fat Exchange, or any combination of these, plus many of the free foods. Salad-making is an artistic challenge, and it can be a pleasure when a few rules are carefully followed.

How to Choose Salad Ingredients:

Many small salads and salad garnishes may be chosen from the Vegetable Exchange List 2B. The familiar tossed salad, combining several raw vegetables and a suitable dressing, is always in good taste, and gives scope for plenty of variety. Vegetables from Vegetable Exchange List 2A can be used raw or cooked, to make additional varieties of mixed salads.

When using a Vegetable Exchange for a salad, you will get more variety by considering the exchange in two, three, or four parts. By referring to your Exchange lists, you can estimate ¼ of the amounts for four different vegetables, and these can be combined to make a delicious salad.

Example:

A Combination of the Following:

> ¼ raw tomato (medium size)
> ¼ green pepper (medium size)
> ⅛ cup shredded raw cabbage
> 1 large lettuce leaf
> will equal 1 Vegetable Exchange List 2B. The tomato and pepper can be chopped and combined with the cabbage, a dressing added if desired (and if allowed), and this can be served on the crisp lettuce leaf.

Additional suggested combinations from Vegetable Exchange List 2B include:

— lettuce, cucumber, celery, and green pepper.
— chicory, tomato, and radish.
— lettuce, parsley, raw cauliflower, and tomato.
— endive, tomato, and cucumber.
— cabbage, celery, and green pepper.
— lettuce, watercress, and cucumber.
— lettuce, raw spinach, and radish.

Similarly, a Fruit Exchange can be divided to include two or more fruits. But, any part of the Fruit Exchange should not be substituted for a part of a Vegetable Exchange and vice versa. Each type of exchange must be calculated separately, even though the foods are finally combined into a mixed salad.

When meat, fish, poultry, cheese or eggs are used in a main course salad, these must also be calculated in terms of a Meat Exchange. In making jellied salads, plain gelatin or artificially sweetened jelly powders should be used, so that exchange values are not affected.

Since most salads are marinated or garnished with a dressing, it is important to remember to calculate the value of the dressing. A simple oil and vinegar dressing, a French dressing, or a mayonnaise dressing may be used, depending upon the amount needed and the fat allowance in your meal plan.

General Rules For Salad Preparation

1. All ingredients, including greens, fruits and vegetables, should be fresh and of good quality.
2. Use fruits and vegetables in season whenever possible, for best quality, flavour and economy.
3. Wash and trim lettuce and celery as soon as you return from shopping. Store in plastic bags or covered containers in the refrigerator.
4. Wash, trim and drain watercress, parsley, radishes, etc. and store in crisper or covered containers in refrigerator.
5. Wash and trim cabbage, crisp in ice water and drain before using.

6. To retain crispness, greens and other fresh vegetables and fruits should be mixed with dressing just before serving. Cooked vegetables, meats, fish and poultry may be marinated ahead of serving time to improve flavour of the salad mixture.
7. Retain the fresh, natural colour of peeled or sliced fruits (pears, peaches and apples) by covering them with water to which salt, lemon juice or vinegar has been added. Drain well before using.

Salad Garnishes

The garnish on the salad should be simple, but should complement the ingredients by making them more attractive and palatable. There is an old-fashioned rule which says, "Every garnish must be edible." You will agree this seems a sensible guide in all food preparation. Calorie Free Food List A and Calorie Poor Food List B should be chosen as garnishes whenever possible. In addition, small portions of vegetables from Vegetable Exchange List 2B may be allowed for garnishes. The following suggestions will help you to choose:

Calorie Free Foods List A — No Food Value:

Horseradish; mushrooms; parsley; and watercress.

Calorie Poor Foods List B:

Cranberries (unsweetened); catsup (1 tsp.); lemon juice (1 tbsp.); prepared mustard (1 tsp.); lemon wedge or twists; dill pickle (1 med.); sour pickles (4 pieces); dietetic sweet mixed pickles (4 pieces); pimento or chopped green pepper (1 tbsp.).

Vegetable Exchange List 2B:

Small portions of the following: Celery heart, stick or fan; green pepper diamonds, strip or rings; cucumber sticks, twists or fluted slices; 1 small green onion; I slice onion, or 1 tsp. chopped onion; radish roses, slices or fans; thin slice or small wedge of tomato; small serving of lettuce.

Salad Dressings

Study your Fat Exchange List in the Meal Planning Booklet for Diabetics in Canada.

If your meal plan includes enough Fat Exchanges to allow a dressing on your salad, keep the following points in mind:
1. One tsp. of vegetable oil provides 1 Fat Exchange, and it may be mixed with vinegar (Calorie Free Food) or lemon juice (Calorie Poor Food) and herbs, or seasonings to make a tasty dressing.
2. One tbsp. of commercial French dressing provides 1 Fat Exchange.
3. One tsp. of commercial mayonnaise provides 1 Fat Exchange.
4. One rounded tbsp. of whipped cream, with artificial liquid sweetener, provides 1 Fat Exchange, as used on a fruit salad.
5. One tbsp. lemon juice (Calorie Poor Food) may be used to dress greens or tossed salad mixtures.

FRUIT SALAD DRESSING

Yield: ½ cup (approximately)
Exchange 1 tbsp. for: 1 Calorie Poor Food List B
Ingredients: 1 tbsp. gelatin
1 tbsp. cold water
¼ cup boiling water
1 tbsp. artificial liquid sweetener
¼ tsp. salt
¼ cup lemon juice
⅛ tsp. dry mustard
½ tsp. paprika
Method: 1. Soften gelatin in cold water; dissolve in boiling water.
2. Combine remaining ingredients and mix with dissolved gelatin; refrigerate; firms when cold; reheat to liquify.

LEMON JUICE DRESSING

Yield: 1⅛ cups
Exchange 1 tbsp. for: 1 Calorie Free Food List A
Ingredients: ½ cup lemon juice
2 tbsps. salad oil
½ cup water
½ tsp. salt
¼ tsp. pepper
½ tsp. celery salt
¼ tsp. dry mustard
Method: 1. Put all ingredients in a jar; close securely with tight-fitting lid.
2. When ready to serve shake vigorously. (For more stability combine ingredients in an electric blender.)

TOMATO FRENCH DRESSING

Yield: 1 cup
Exchange 1 tbsp. for: 1 Calorie Poor Food List B
Ingredients: ½ cup canned condensed tomato soup, undiluted
¼ cup water
2 tbsps. vinegar
1 tbsp. grated onion
2 tbsps. finely chopped green pepper
1 tsp. Worcestershire sauce
½ tsp. salt
½ tsp. dry mustard
⅛ tsp. garlic powder
¼ tsp. artificial liquid sweetener
Method: Prepare as for lemon juice dressing.

BOILED DRESSING (COOKED SALAD DRESSING)

Yield: 1 cup

Exchange 1 tbsp. for: 1 Calorie Poor Food List B

Ingredients: ⅓ cup skim milk powder
⅓ cup water
2 eggs
1 tsp. salt
½ tsp. paprika
½ tsp. dry mustard
dash cayenne pepper
2 tbsps. cider vinegar or lemon juice

Method:
1. Mix milk powder and water.
2. Beat eggs lightly in top of double boiler.
3. Blend in milk, salt, and spices.
4. Gradually add vinegar, stirring to blend.
5. Place over hot water; cook, stirring constantly until thickened.
6. Cool and refrigerate.

Variation: 1 tbsp. salad oil may be stirred into dressing after it is cooked and removed from the heat; chill and keep refrigerated.

APPLE AND CELERY SALAD

Yield: 1 serving

Exchange for: 1 Fruit Exchange
and 1 Fat Exchange
and ½ Vegetable Exchange List 2B

Ingredients: ½ medium-sized apple, brightly coloured
¼ cup diced raw celery
1 tsp. mayonnaise, diluted with a little lemon juice

Method:
1. Leaving skin on, wash apple and cut in half.
2. Remove core, stem and calyx, and cut ½ apple into small cubes.
3. Add diced celery and mayonnaise, diluted with lemon juice.
4. Mix thoroughly and marinate for few minutes before serving.
5. Serve on a crisp lettuce cup.

MACARONI SALAD

Yield: 1 serving
Exchange for: 1 Bread Exchange
and 1 Meat Exchange
and 1 Fat Exchange
and 1 Vegetable Exchange List 2B
Ingredients: ½ cup cooked macaroni
1 tbsp. lemon juice
1 tsp. salad oil
1 stalk celery, chopped
1 green onion, chopped
1 tbsp. pimento, chopped
¼ cup diced cooked ham
1 tsp. prepared mustard
salt and pepper to taste
Method: 1. Cook macaroni in large amount of boiling salted water. (¼ cup of uncooked macaroni will yield about ½ cup cooked macaroni); drain in a sieve under cold running water; drain well.
2. Beat lemon juice and salad oil together; toss into the macaroni and cover; chill macaroni for several hours.
3. Add chopped celery, chopped green onion, chopped pimento, diced ham and prepared mustard.
4. Add salt and pepper to taste.
5. Serve on a leaf of lettuce.

POTATO SALAD

Yield: 1 serving
Exchange for: 1 Bread Exchange
Or 2 Vegetable Exchanges List 2A
Ingredients: 1 small chilled, boiled potato
½ tsp. finely chopped onion
1 tsp. chopped pimento
dressing to moisten. See pages 76 and 77.
salt and pepper to taste
Method: 1. Dice potato and mix with other ingredients.
2. Chill well before serving.
Note: Check values of dressing used and add 1 Fat Exchange, if necessary, to account for dressing used.
Variations: 1. Small amounts of chopped celery, parsley or green pepper may be added without altering exchange values.
2. Add 1 hard-cooked egg, sliced, or ¼ cup diced cooked ham or bologna, or 5 small cooked shrimps, and increase exchange value by adding 1 Meat Exchange.

GREEN BEAN SALAD

Yield: 4 servings

Exchange 1 serving for: 1 Vegetable Exchange List 2B
and 1 Fat Exchange

Ingredients: 1½ cups canned or cooked green beans, drained
½ small onion, thinly sliced and separated into rings
1 tbsp. chopped pimento
¼ cup French dressing. See page 76.
¼ tsp. garlic salt
dash black pepper

Method: 1. Combine all ingredients.
2. Cover; let stand in refrigerator overnight.

Variation: ¼ cup cooked or canned sliced mushrooms, drained, may
be added to bean mixture before refrigerating.

CHICKEN, SALMON, OR TUNA FISH SALAD

Yield: 1 serving

Exchange for: 2 Meat Exchanges
Add 1 Fat Exchange if 1 tsp. commercial mayonnaise
is used or add the exchange value of the amount of
other salad dressing used.

Ingredients: ½ cup diced, cooked chicken, or drained, flaked salmon
or tuna fish
1 tbsp. chopped celery
1 tsp. chopped onion or green pepper, if desired
salt and pepper to taste
salad dressing or mayonnaise to moisten. See page 76.

Method: 1. Combine all ingredients.
2. Chill and serve with salad greens or lettuce.

DEVILLED EGGS

Yield: 1 egg (2 halves) equals 1 serving

Exchange 1 egg for: 1 Meat Exchange
Add 1 Fat Exchange if 1 tsp. commercial mayonnaise is used or add the exchange value for the
amount of other salad dressing used.

Ingredients: 1 hard-cooked egg
salt and other seasonings such as pepper, vinegar, horseradish
pinch of dry mustard
salad dressing or mayonnaise to moisten. See page 76.
paprika for garnish

Method: 1. Peel and cut egg either crosswise or lengthwise.
2. Remove yolk and mash with a fork.
3. Add salt, seasonings and mustard to egg yolk.
4. Moisten with salad dressing.
5. Refill egg white with yolk mixture.
6. Garnish with paprika.

GELATIN SALADS

Using unflavoured gelatin or artifically sweetened jelly powders as bases, a variety of delicious jellied salads may be made. Exchange values of the salads will depend upon the ingredients. Jellied salads should be well chilled and kept cold until serving time.

TOMATO ASPIC MADE WITH TOMATO JUICE

Yield: 2 servings

Exchange 1 serving for: 1 Vegetable Exchange List 2B

Ingredients: 1 cup tomato juice
dash of salt
dash of celery salt
1 tsp. chopped onion
1 whole clove
small piece of bay leaf
2 tsps. vinegar
1 envelope artifically sweetened lemon jelly powder

Method: 1. Combine tomato juice and all seasonings in a saucepan.
2. Cover and bring to a boil.
3. Remove from heat and pour over artifically sweetened jelly powder, stirring until dissolved.
4. Cover and let stand 5 minutes.
5. Strain and divide evenly into 2 moulds.
6. Chill until firm.

FRENCH TOMATO ASPIC

Yield: 6 servings
Exchange 1 serving for: 1 Vegetable Exchange List 2B
Ingredients: 1 tbsp. unflavoured gelatin
2 cups mixed vegetable juice
2 tsps. clear commercial French dressing
Method: 1. Sprinkle gelatin into ¼ cup cold mixed vegetable juice.
2. Bring remaining mixed vegetable juice to a boil.
3. Add to softened gelatin, stirring until gelatin is dissolved.
4. Add 2 tsps. clear commercial French dressing.
5. Divide into 6 individual moulds.
6. Chill until firm; unmould and place each serving on a lettuce leaf.

CONFETTI SALAD

Yield: 2 servings
Exchange 1 serving for: 1 Calorie Poor Food List B
Ingredients: 1 envelope artifically sweetened lemon jelly powder
1 cup hot water
⅛ tsp. salt
¼ tsp. grated onion
¼ cup (30 gms.) very small pieces of raw cauliflower or shredded cabbage
2 tsps. (10 gms.) diced pimento
Method: 1. Dissolve jelly powder in hot water.
2. Add salt and onion.
3. Chill until slightly thickened.
4. Fold in cauliflower and pimento.
5. Divide evenly into 2 moulds.
6. Chill until firm.
7. Unmould on crisp greens.
8. Serve with low-calorie mayonnaise or dressing.

JELLIED SPRING VEGETABLE SALAD

Yield: 6 servings
Exchange 1 serving for: 1 Calorie Poor Food List B
Ingredients: 1½ tbsps. unflavoured gelatin
¼ cup cold water
2 cups boiling water
½ tsp. salt
¼ cup unsweetened lime juice
2 tsps. artificial liquid sweetener
few drops green food colouring
1 cup diced, peeled cucumber
1 cup sliced radishes
¼ cup sliced green onions

Method: 1. Soften gelatin in cold water; dissolve in boiling water.

2. Add salt, lime juice, and artificial liquid sweetener.

3. Chill until mixture begins to thicken.

4. Fold in remaining ingredients.

5. Pour into a 3-cup mould or divide evenly into 6 individual moulds.

6. Chill until firm; unmould on crisp greens.

PERFECTION SALAD

Yield: 4 servings

Exchange 1 serving for: 1 Calorie Poor Food List B

Ingredients: ⅓ cup diluted vinegar
1⅓ cups boiling water
¾ tsp. salt
½ tsp. artificial liquid sweetener
1⅓ tbsps. unflavoured gelatin
⅓ cup cold water
juice of 1 lemon
⅔ cup shredded cabbage
1½ cups diced celery
2 tbsps. chopped green pepper or pimento
1 or 2 drops green food colouring, if desired

Method: 1. Mix boiling water, vinegar, and salt; heat to boiling point.

2. Soften gelatin in cold water; dissolve in boiling liquid after it is removed from the stove.

3. Add lemon juice and artificial liquid sweetener.

4. When slightly thickened, add vegetables.

5. Divide into four moistened moulds; chill until firm.

JELLIED CRANBERRY SALAD

Yield: 4 servings

Exchange 1 serving for: 1 Vegetable Exchange List 2B

Ingredients: 1 tbsp. unflavoured gelatin
¼ cup cold water
1½ cups cranberries (raw)
½ cup boiling water
2 tsps. lemon juice
1½ tsps. artificial liquid sweetener
⅛ tsp. salt
½ cup celery cut crosswise in ⅛ inch slices

Method: 1. Soften gelatin in cold water.
2. Put cranberries and boiling water in a pan with tight-fitting lid and boil until the berries pop open.
3. Put through sieve. Measure juice and pulp; add water if necessary to make 1 cup.
4. Heat this to the boiling point; add to gelatin and stir until dissolved.
5. Add lemon juice, sweetener and salt.
6. Pour into a mould, and when mixture is slightly thickened, fold in sliced celery.
7. Chill until firm; unmould and place on lettuce leaf.

Variation: Fold in 1 medium apple (diced), *or* 1 cup dietetic crushed pineapple along with the celery.
Increase exchange value by ½ Fruit Exchange.

Suggestions for serving: If fat allowance permits serve with 1 tsp. commercial mayonnaise (add 1 Fat Exchange).

GRAPE AND GRAPEFRUIT GELATIN SALAD

Yield: 2 servings

Exchange 1 serving for: ½ Fruit Exchange

Ingredients: 1 tsp. unflavoured gelatin
2 tbsps. cold water
5 tbsps. hot water
2 tbsps. grape juice (unsweetened)
¼ grapefruit, cut into sections
1 tsp. lemon juice
¼ grain tablet artificial sweetener

Method: 1. Soften gelatin in cold water.

2. Heat grape juice with hot water; add to gelatin, and stir until dissolved.

3. Cool.

4. Dissolve sweetener in lemon juice and add to gelatin mixture.

5. Pour into a mould, and when mixture begins to set add the grapefruit sections.

6. Chill until firm, and unmould on crisp greens.

GRAPEFRUIT CRESS SALAD

Yield: 2 servings

Exchange 1 serving for: ½ Fruit Exchange

Ingredients: 1 envelope artificially sweetened lemon jelly powder
dash of salt
1 cup hot water
5 sections (100 gms.) drained, unsweetened grapefruit
¼ cup coarsely cut watercress or celery tops
½ tsp. drained chopped pimento

Method: 1. Dissolve jelly powder and salt in hot water.

2. Chill until slightly thickened.

3. Fold in grapefruit sections (cut in half) watercress and pimento.

4. Divide evenly into 2 moulds.

5. Chill until firm.

6. Unmould on crisp salad greens.

7. Serve with dressing, if allowed.

LIME COTTAGE CHEESE SALAD

Yield: 4 servings

Exchange 1 serving for: ½ Meat Exchange

Ingredients: 2 envelopes or 1 tbsp. artificially sweetened lime jelly powder

2 cups hot water

2 tsps. vinegar

⅛ tsp. salt

½ cup cottage cheese

2 tsps. pimento

1 tsp. grated onion

Method: 1. Dissolve jelly powder in hot water.
2. Stir in vinegar and salt.
3. Pour 1 cup of this mixture into a mould.
4. Chill until almost firm.
5. At the same time, chill remaining cup of jelly base until slightly thickened.
6. Into it, fold cheese, pimento and onion.
7. Pour over first jelly layer in mould.
8. Chill until firm, and unmould on crisp greens.

JELLIED CHICKEN AND VEGETABLE SALAD

Yield: 4 servings

Exchange 1 serving for: 1 Meat Exchange
and 1 Vegetable Exchange List 2B

Ingredients: 1 envelope or 1 tbsp. unflavoured gelatin

¼ cup cold water

2 cups fat-free chicken stock

1 cup (4 oz.) cooked, diced chicken.

2 cups of diced celery, green pepper, sliced radishes, and asparagus tips combined

Method: 1. Soften gelatin in cold water.
2. Add hot chicken stock and stir until dissolved.
3. Pour a thin layer of liquid jelly into a mould; let this set slightly.
4. Add a layer of vegetables, then a layer of diced chicken.
5. Add another thin layer of liquid jelly and let it set slightly.
6. Continue these layers until all vegetables, chicken and jelly mixture are used.
7. Chill until firm; unmould and place on a lettuce leaf.

SANDWICHES

Ever since the Earl of Sandwich first introduced his novel idea, its popularity has grown. Many people carry sandwiches in lunch boxes to school, to work, or on picnics. At afternoon teas or evening parties, sandwiches, hot or cold, plain or fancy, large or small, are often more attractive than cakes. This trend should please the diabetic, who will have to forego the cake, but can pick and choose from the sandwich tray.

Included on the following pages are suggestions for sandwich fillings which may be made at home, but which can also be ordered from a restaurant menu. In addition, suggestions are included for hamburgers and hot dogs.

The amount of bread or roll used in making the sandwiches, hamburgers or hot dogs will depend on the bread allowance for the meal. Many of the fillings make up well in an open-faced sandwich which requires only one slice of bread or ½ hamburger bun or ½ wiener roll.

EGG SALAD FILLING

Yield: 1 serving
Exchange for: 1 Meat Exchange
and 1 Fat Exchange
Ingredients: 1 egg, hard cooked
pinch of dry mustard
½ tsp. chopped onion, celery, or green pepper
1 tsp. mayonnaise
salt and pepper to taste
Method: 1. Mash egg with a fork.
2. Add seasonings, mayonnaise, chopped onion, etc.
3. Mix well; refrigerate until time of serving.

SALMON, TUNA OR LOBSTER FILLING

Yield: 1 serving
Exchange for: 1 Meat Exchange
           and 1 Fat Exchange
Ingredients: ¼ cup of cooked or canned salmon, tuna, or lobster
           1 tsp. chopped celery
           ½ tsp. chopped onion for flavouring
           1 tsp. mayonnaise
           lemon juice or vinegar
           salt and pepper to taste
Method: 1. Flake fish with a fork.
        2. Mix well with other ingredients.
        3. Refrigerate until time of serving.
Note: The mayonnaise may be omitted if desired, in which case the exchange for the filling would be only 1 Meat Exchange.

CHICKEN SALAD FILLING

Yield: 1 serving
Exchange for: 1 Meat Exchange
           and 1 Fat Exchange
Ingredients: ¼ cup cooked chopped, or minced chicken
           1 tsp. chopped celery
           1 tsp. mayonnaise
           salt and pepper to taste
Method: 1. Mix all ingredients until well blended.
        2. Refrigerate until time of serving.

MINCED BEEF, VEAL OR HAM FILLING

Yield: 1 serving
Exchange for: 1 Meat Exchange
           and 1 Fat Exchange
Ingredients: ¼ cup minced beef, veal, or ham
           ½ tsp. chopped onion
           ½ tsp. chopped unsweetened pickle
           pinch of mustard
           1 tsp. mayonnaise
           salt and pepper to taste
Method: 1. Mix all ingredients until well blended.
        2. Refrigerate until time of serving.

COLD SLICED CHICKEN, BEEF, VEAL, LAMB OR HAM FILLING

Yield: 1 serving
Exchange for: 2 Meat Exchanges
Ingredients: 2 slices of any of the above meats, each slice measuring
4" x 2" x ¼"
salt and pepper to taste
lettuce, if desired
Note: With beef, a little horseradish may be used — Calorie Poor Food List B.
With ham or beef, a little mustard may be used — prepared mustard, or home-made mustard — Calorie Poor Food List B.
With chicken, mayonnaise may be used, in which case the exchange would be: 2 Meat Exchanges
and 1 Fat Exchange

GRILLED CHEESE SANDWICH

Yield: 1 sandwich
Exchange for: 1 Meat Exchange
and 2 Bread Exchanges
Ingredients: 2 slices bread
1 slice of pre-sliced processed cheese
Method: 1. Place cheese between two slices of bread.
2. Toast in sandwich toaster, grill, or brown in hot oven (400°F-425°F), turning during the cooking.

GRILLED CHEESE AND BACON SANDWICH

Yield: 1 sandwich
Exchange for: 2 Meat Exchanges
and 1 Bread Exchange
Ingredients: 1 slice of pre-sliced processed cheese
3 strips bacon, partially cooked and cut in half
1 slice bread
Method: 1. Place cheese on top of bread.
2. Place partially cooked bacon on top of cheese.
3. Broil, or finish cooking in hot oven (400°F-425°F) until bacon is cooked and cheese melting.
Note: Ham, or other meat may be used in place of bacon, in which case place meat next to the bread, and the cheese on top of the meat, with a little catsup or mustard, or slice of tomato on top for extra flavour.

WESTERN SANDWICH

Yield: 1 sandwich
Exchange for: 2 Meat Exchanges
and 1 Fat Exchange
and 2 Bread Exchanges
Ingredients: 3 strips crisp bacon, cut into small pieces
or ¼ cup diced cooked ham
1 tsp. chopped onion
1 egg
salt and pepper to taste
2 slices bread or toast
Method: 1. Cook bacon pieces; remove from pan.
2. Drain fat from pan, leaving 1 tsp. in which to cook the chopped onion until lightly browned.
3. Break egg into frying pan; add cooked bacon, salt and pepper; stir briskly to mix all ingredients and keep egg from sticking to pan; cook until egg is firm, but not hard.
4. Serve between 2 slices bread or toast.

TOASTED SARDINE SANDWICH

Yield: 1 sandwich
Exchange for: 3 Meat Exchanges
and 1 Bread Exchange
and 1 Fat Exchange
Ingredients: 6 sardines in mustard sauce
1 tsp. butter or margarine
1 slice bread
1 slice pre-sliced processed cheese
paprika to garnish
Method: 1. Drain sardines; mix ½ tsp. mustard sauce with softened butter or margarine and spread on bread.
2. Arrange sardines on bread and top with sliced cheese.
3. Sprinkle with paprika.
4. Toast in hot oven (400°F to 425°F) for several minutes, or until cheese begins to melt.

HAMBURGER

Yield: 1 serving
Exchange for: 2 Meat Exchanges
and 2 Bread Exchanges
and 1 Fat Exchange
Ingredients: 6 tbsps. raw lean minced beef
salt and pepper to taste
1 tsp. butter or margarine
1 hamburger bun

Method: 1. Form seasoned minced beef into a meat patty.
2. Broil in oven or pan broil on top of stove.
3. Split and butter bun and warm in oven if desired.
4. Place meat patty in bun and serve hot with one or more of the following, according to food allowance:

1 slice tomato — 1 Calorie Poor Food List B.
1 slice onion — 1 Vegetable Exchange List 2B.
Cole slaw, ⅓ to ½ cup — 1 Vegetable Exchange List 2B.
1 tsp. catsup — 1 Calorie Poor Food List B.
½ to 1 tsp. mustard — 1 Calorie Poor Food List B.
3 or 4 slices unsweetened dill pickles — 1 Calorie Poor Food List B.

Variations: The meat patty may be varied without appreciably changing its exchange value by adding to the minced beef before broiling one or two of the following:

½ tsp. finely chopped onion
½ tsp. finely chopped green pepper
¼ tsp. Worcestershire sauce
⅛ to ¼ tsp. horseradish
½ tsp. hamburger relish

TUNA BURGERS

Yield: 6 servings
Exchange 1 serving for: 2 Meat Exchanges
and 2 Bread Exchanges
and 2 Fat Exchanges
and 1 Calorie Poor Food List B

Ingredients: one 7-oz. tin tuna fish, drained and flaked
¾ cup chopped celery
1 small onion, diced
½ cup diced cheese
½ cup chopped olives
3 tbsps. mayonnaise
salt and pepper to taste
6 hamburger buns

Method: 1. Mix tuna fish, celery, onion, cheese, olives, mayonnaise, salt and pepper.
2. Split 6 hamburger buns.
3. Divide tuna filling evenly among six buns.
4. Place buns in dampened paper sandwich bags or wrap in aluminum foil, folding and fastening with paper clips.
5. Heat in oven at 350°F for 15 to 20 minutes; serve hot.

CHEESEBURGER

Yield: 1 serving

Exchange for: 2 Meat Exchanges
and 1 Bread Exchange
and 2 Fat Exchanges

Ingredients: 3 tbsps. raw lean minced beef
½ tsp. grated onion, if desired
salt and pepper to taste
1 tsp. butter or margarine
1 slice pre-sliced processed cheese
1 strip side bacon
½ hamburger bun

Method: 1. Add grated onion and seasonings to beef; shape into patty.

2. Cook under broiler, or if desired, cook in frying pan with the 1 tsp. butter or margarine and a little water, if necessary, to keep it from sticking to the pan.

3. Place cooked meat patty on half hamburger bun.

4. Top with slice of cheese and strip of bacon, cut in half.

5. Place in oven under broiler until the bacon is cooked. If you do not have a broiler, partially cook bacon before placing it on top of cheese, and then put cheeseburger in hot oven (400°F to 425°F) until bacon is cooked.

Note: 1 tsp. butter or margarine has been allowed. It may be used when (1) cooking the meat patty or (2) to butter the bun or (3) it may be omitted entirely. If it is omitted, the exchange of fat would only be ONE instead of two Fat Exchanges. If the meal plan allows 2 Bread Exchanges, a whole hamburger bun may be used instead of ½ bun. The top of the bun should not be put on the cheeseburger until the bacon is cooked.

HAM ROLL

Yield: 1 serving

Exchange for: 1 Bread Exchange
and 1 Meat Exchange
and 1 Fat Exchange

Ingredients: ¼ cup minced cooked ham
1 tsp. chopped celery
1 tsp. mayonnaise
salt and pepper to taste
1 parkerhouse roll

Method: 1. Mix first 4 ingredients.

2. Place filling in parkerhouse roll which has been split lengthwise.

3. Place in oven which has been heated to 375°F, for about 5 minutes, or until the roll and filling have been heated through.

4. Serve hot.

Note: Chicken or fish filling may be used in place of the ham, using same amount.

HOT DOG

Yield: 1 serving

Exchange for: 1 Meat Exchange
and 2 Bread Exchanges
and 1 Calorie Poor Food List B

Ingredients: 1 wiener
1 wiener roll
½ to 1 tsp. mustard, catsup or other meat sauce

Method: 1. Boil or broil wiener.

2. Place in a split wiener roll which has been heated.

3. Serve with mustard or other meat sauce of your choice.

HOT DOG DELIGHT

Yield: 1 serving

Exchange for: 2 Meat Exchanges
and 1 Fat Exchange
and 2 Bread Exchanges

Ingredients: 1 wiener, cooked
1 slice pre-sliced processed cheese
1 strip partially cooked bacon
1 wiener roll

Method: 1. Roll cheese around wiener which has been cooked, and roll partially cooked bacon around both cheese and wiener.
2. Fasten with a toothpick.
3. Broil for 1 to 2 minutes.
4. Place on a heated wiener bun.

ROLLED PARTY SANDWICH

Yield: 1 serving

Exchange for: ½ Bread Exchange
and 1 Fat Exchange
and 1 Calorie Poor Food List B

Ingredients: 1 slice sandwich bread
1 tsp. commercial mayonnaise
1 stalk canned or cooked asparagus

Method: 1. Trim crust from moist sandwich bread.
2. Roll bread with rolling pin to prevent cracking.
3. Spread mayonnaise thinly on bread being sure to spread it right to the edges.
4. Place stalk of asparagus at one side of bread and roll up closely.
5. Place with open edge of roll down and cover with damp tea towel; refrigerate until serving time.

Variation: Use 1 tbsp. cream cheese and a piece of celery in place of the 1 tsp. of mayonnaise and the stalk of asparagus.

OPEN-FACED FRUIT PARTY SANDWICH

Yield: 1 serving

Exchange for: ½ Bread Exchange
and 1 Fat Exchange
and ¼ Fruit Exchange

Ingredients: 1 slice of sandwich bread
1 tbsp. of cream cheese (white)
3 canned dietetic mandarin orange sections

Method: 1. Trim crusts from bread.
2. Spread bread with softened cream cheese.
3. Cut bread into triangles or fingers.
4. Cut mandarin orange sections into pieces and arrange on bread in an attractive manner.
5. Cover with damp tea towel and keep in the refrigerator until serving time. It is best, however, to serve these sandwiches soon after preparation.

Variations: 1. In place of the 3 canned dietetic mandarin orange sections you may use 3 grapes (cut in half) *or* ¼ grapefruit cut in sections.
2. For variety you may tint the cream cheese with food colouring or add 1 teaspoon of artificially sweetened jam spread.

OPEN-FACED EGG PARTY SANDWICH

Yield: 1 serving

Exchange for: ½ Bread Exchange
and 1 Fat Exchange
and 1 Meat Exchange

Ingredients: 1 slice of sandwich bread
filling from Egg Salad Sandwich Filling. See page 87.
1 tsp. of finely diced pimento, sour pickles or green pepper

Method: 1. Trim crusts from bread.
2. Spread bread with filling.
3. Cut bread into triangles or fingers.
4. Decorate with small pieces of pimento, or sour pickles, or chopped green pepper.
5. Cover with damp tea towel; refrigerate until serving time.

Variations: Instead of egg salad sandwich filling use:
Salmon, Tuna, or Lobster Filling
or Chicken Salad Sandwich Filling
or Minced Beef, Veal or Ham Filling. See page 88.

DESSERTS

"The mission of dessert is being that of a comforter of the stomach which being already appeased, nevertheless requires a little reflex flattery."

Raw fruit may be nature's perfect dessert — and instant too — but have a change now and again and try some of the following recipes.

They are divided according to the Exchanges they will provide — fruit, milk or combinations — so plan your meal accordingly.

Do not forget you will still need your Fruit Exchange in addition, if the dessert you choose does not provide it.

FRUIT EXCHANGE DESSERTS
BAKED APPLE

Yield: 1 serving
Exchange for: 1 Fruit Exchange
Ingredients: 1 small apple
           f.g. cinnamon and nutmeg
           1 tbsp. orange juice (unsweetened)
           ¼ tsp. artificial liquid sweetener
           ¼ cup water
Method: 1. Wash and core apple; score skin to prevent bursting.
         2. Place in baking dish; sprinkle with cinnamon and nutmeg.
         3. Combine orange juice, artificial liquid sweetener and water; pour over apple.
         4. Bake at 350°F about 45 minutes.

JELLIED FRUITS

For a simple jellied fruit dessert, combine any fruit or combination of fruits in amounts allowed on the diet with any artificially sweetened jelly powder you like and count as a Fruit Exchange.

Alternatively, try one of the following whips and count the Fruit Exchange as shown.

FRUIT WHIP (Basic Recipe)

Yield: 6 servings

Exchange 1 serving for: See exchange below, opposite name of fruit you select

Ingredients: 1 tbsp. or 1 envelope unflavoured gelatin
¼ cup cold water
¼ cup boiling water
fruit (see below for a variety of fruits to use)
2 tbsps. lemon juice
1 tsp. grated lemon rind
1 tsp. vanilla or flavouring of choice
1½ tsps. artificial liquid sweetener
2 egg whites
⅛ tsp. salt

Method:
1. Soften gelatin in cold water.
2. Add boiling water and stir until dissolved.
3. Add fruit (see below), lemon juice, lemon rind, vanilla and artificial liquid sweetener; mix well.
4. Chill until partially set; whip until frothy.
5. Beat egg whites and salt until stiff; whip these ingredients into gelatin mixture until jelly holds its shape.
6. Pile into serving dishes; chill.

VARIATIONS:

Apple: — Use 1½ cups unsweetened applesauce.
   Exchange 1 serving for: ½ Fruit Exchange.
Apricot: — Use 1 cup apricot pulp. One 16 oz. can of drained, dietetic apricots yields 1 cup pulp.
   Exchange 1 serving for: ½ Fruit Exchange.
Banana: — Use 1 cup banana pulp. (3 medium bananas)
   Exchange 1 serving for: 1 Fruit Exchange.
Prune: — Use ⅓ cup prune pulp (12 cooked, pitted prunes). Dilute this with 1 cup unsweetened prune juice.
   Exchange 1 serving for: 1 Fruit Exchange.

MILK EXCHANGE DESSERTS

Although **whole milk** is specified in many of these recipes, you may use **2% milk** or **skim milk** if your meal plan indicates either of these types. Where **evaporated milk** is specified in a recipe, it should be used; replacing it with another type of milk will affect the success of the recipe.

QUICK VANILLA PUDDING

Yield: 6 servings

Exchange 1 serving for: 1 Milk Exchange

Ingredients: 2 tbsps. or 2 envelopes unflavoured gelatin
     ⅓ cup cold water
     ½ cup boiling water
     3 cups whole milk
     1 tbsp. vanilla
     1 tbsp. artificial liquid sweetener
     ⅛ tsp. salt

Method: 1. Soften gelatin in cold water.
     2. Add boiling water and stir until dissolved.
     3. Add all other ingredients; mix well.
     4. Pour into serving dishes; chill.

JUNKET

Yield: 4 servings

Exchange 1 serving for: 1 Milk Exchange

Ingredients: 1 junket tablet
     1 tbsp. cold water
     1 tsp. artificial liquid sweetener
     2 cups whole milk
     1 tsp. vanilla

Method: 1. Set out 4 dessert dishes.
     2. Dissolve junket tablet in cold water.
     3. Add artificial liquid sweetener.
     4. Heat milk and vanilla (**or** choice of flavouring and colouring as below) to lukewarm (110°F); remove from heat.
     5. Add dissolved junket tablet; stir for few seconds only.
     6. Pour immediately into individual serving dishes.
     7. Allow to stand undisturbed until firm; chill.

Variations: 1. Almond cream _____ ½ tsp. almond extract, 2 drops yellow food colouring

     Lemon cream _____ ½ tsp. lemon extract, several drops yellow food colouring

     Orange cream _____ 1 tsp. orange extract, 2 - 3 drops orange food colouring

     Peppermint cream _____ ⅛ tsp. peppermint extract, 2 - 3 drops red food colouring

     2. Add fruit from
     Fruit Exchange _____ put fruit in bottom of individual dessert dishes before making junket. Pour over fruit.

BAKED CUSTARD

Yield: 6 servings

Exchange 1 serving for: 1 Milk Exchange

Ingredients: 2 eggs
¼ tsp. salt
2 cups whole milk
1 tsp. vanilla
1 tsp. artificial liquid sweetener
nutmeg

Method: 1. Beat eggs slightly; add salt.
2. Pour scalded milk slowly over eggs, beating with a fork to keep smooth.
3. Add vanilla and artificial liquid sweetener.
4. Pour into custard cups; sprinkle with nutmeg.
5. Set cups in a shallow pan of hot water.
6. Bake at 325°F about 30 minutes or until a table knife inserted into custard comes out clean.

CHOCOLATE PUDDING

Yield: 6 servings

Exchange 1 serving for: 1 Milk Exchange

Ingredients: 2 tbsps. or 2 envelopes unflavoured gelatin
⅓ cup cold water
3 tbsps. cocoa
1 tbsp. artificial liquid sweetener
⅛ tsp. salt
¼ tsp. vanilla
⅛ tsp. cinnamon
3 cups whole milk

Method: 1. Soften gelatin in cold water.
2. Make a paste of the next five ingredients using a little of the cold milk.
3. Scald rest of milk and add to paste, stirring constantly.
4. Heat milk mixture to boiling.
5. Add gelatin and stir until dissolved.
6. Pour into moulds or serving dishes; chill.

Note: May be unmoulded for serving, if desired.

FRUIT FLUFF

Yield: 8 servings
Exchange 1 serving for: ½ Milk Exchange
Ingredients: 1 tbsp. or 2 envelopes artificially sweetened jelly powder
    (orange, strawberry, lime, etc.)
    ¾ cup boiling water
    ½ cup applesauce (unsweetened)
    1 tsp. artificial liquid sweetener
    6 oz. evaporated milk (very cold)
    1 tbsp. lemon juice
Method: 1. Dissolve jelly powder in boiling water.
    2. Add applesauce and artificial liquid sweetener; mix well.
    3. Chill until partially set; whip until frothy.
    4. Add lemon juice to evaporated milk and whip until stiff.
    5. Add whipped milk to the jelly mixture and continue to whip until thoroughly mixed and the jelly holds its shape.
    6. Pile into serving dishes; chill.

COMBINED EXCHANGE DESSERTS
SOFT CUSTARD

Yield: 6 servings (2 cups)
Exchange 1 serving (⅓ cup) with whole milk for: ½ Milk Exchange
    and ½ Fat Exchange
(⅓ cup) with skim milk for: ½ Milk Exchange
Ingredients: 3 egg yolks
    ¼ tsp. salt
    2 cups whole or skim milk
    1 tsp. vanilla
    1 tsp. artificial liquid sweetener
Method: 1. Beat egg yolks slightly; add salt.
    2. Pour scalded milk slowly over eggs, beating with a fork to keep smooth.
    3. Cook and stir in double boiler over hot, not boiling water, until mixture coats a spoon (about 7 minutes).
    4. Add vanilla and artificial liquid sweetener; strain and cool.

POMPADOUR CUSTARD

Yield: 6 servings
Exchange 1 serving for: ½ Milk Exchange
    and ½ Meat Exchange
Ingredients: 2 cups Soft Custard. See above.
    3 egg whites
    ⅛ tsp. salt
    ½ tsp. artificial liquid sweetener
    2 tbsps. cocoa

Method:
1. Prepare Soft Custard and place in serving dishes.
2. Beat egg whites and salt until stiff.
3. Add artificial liquid sweetener and cocoa.
4. Place a heaping spoonful of meringue on each dessert.

FLOATING ISLAND

Yield: 6 servings

Exchange 1 serving for: ½ Milk Exchange
and ½ Meat Exchange

Ingredients: 2 cups Soft Custard. See page 100.
3 egg whites
⅛ tsp. salt
½ tsp. artificial liquid sweetener
½ tsp. vanilla

Method:
1. Prepare soft custard and place in a baking dish.
2. Beat egg whites and salt until stiff.
3. Add artificial liquid sweetener and vanilla.
4. Heap the egg whites in 6 mounds on the custard.
5. Bake at 500°F for 2 minutes or under a broiler until the tips of the meringue are brown; serve hot or cold.

SPANISH CREAM

Yield: 6 servings

Exchange 1 serving for: ½ Milk Exchange
and ½ Meat Exchange

Ingredients: 1 tbsp. or 1 envelope unflavoured gelatin
2 cups whole milk
3 eggs, separated
½ tsp. salt
1 tsp. vanilla
2 tsps. artificial liquid sweetener

Method:
1. Soften gelatin using ¼ cup of the cold milk.
2. Beat egg yolks slightly; add ¼ tsp. salt.
3. Scald remaining milk; pour slowly over eggs, beating with a fork to keep smooth.
4. Cook and stir in double boiler over hot, not boiling, water until mixture coats a spoon (about 7 minutes).
5. Add gelatin and stir until dissolved.
6. Add vanilla and artificial liquid sweetener.
7. Beat egg whites and ¼ tsp. salt until stiff; fold into milk mixture.
8. Pour into mould or bowl dipped in cold water; refrigerate.

Note: As Spanish Cream cools it divides into 2 layers.

APPLE MOUSSE

Yield: 6 servings

Exchange 1 serving for: ½ Milk Exchange
and ½ Fruit Exchange

Ingredients: 6 oz. evaporated milk (very cold)
1 tbsp. lemon juice
1½ tsps. artificial liquid sweetener
½ tsp. nutmeg
½ tsp. salt
1½ cups applesauce (unsweetened)

Method: 1. Add lemon juice to evaporated milk and whip until stiff.
2. Add artificial liquid sweetener, nutmeg and salt to apple-sauce; fold into whipped milk.
3. Pile into 6 moulds or into a tray and freeze until firm.
4. Unmould, or cut it in a tray, and serve.

RICE PINEAPPLE DESSERT

Yield: 6 servings

Exchange 1 serving for: 1 Milk Exchange
and 1 Fruit Exchange

Ingredients: 1½ tbsps. or 1½ envelopes unflavoured gelatin
⅓ cup cold water
½ cup boiling water
1⅓ cups cooked rice
1½ tsps. artificial liquid sweetener
1 cup dietetic crushed pineapple (drained)
pinch of salt
6 oz. evaporated milk (very cold)
1 tbsp. lemon juice

Method: 1. Soften gelatin in cold water.
2. Add boiling water and stir until dissolved.
3. Add cooked rice, artificial liquid sweetener, pineapple and salt; mix well.
4. Add lemon juice to evaporated milk and whip until stiff; fold into rice mixture.
5. Pile into serving dishes; chill.

Variations: 1 cup dietetic fruit cocktail, drained, may be used in place of pineapple.

ORANGE CREAM PUDDING

Yield: 6 servings

Exchange 1 serving for: 1 Milk Exchange
and ½ Fruit Exchange

Ingredients: 3 tbsps. cornstarch
⅛ tsp. salt
2 tsps. artificial liquid sweetener
3 cups whole milk
grated rind of one orange
1 tsp. vanilla
few drops orange food colouring
1 orange in sections

Method: 1. Make a paste of the first 3 ingredients, using ½ cup of the milk.
2. Scald rest of the milk and orange rind and add to the paste, stirring constantly.
3. Stir and cook milk mixture over boiling water, until fully thickened.
4. Add vanilla and food colouring.
5. Pour into serving dishes and garnish with orange sections; chill.

TART SHELLS (PASTRY)

Yield: 12 shells

Exchange 1 tart shell for: ½ Bread Exchange
and 1 Fat Exchange

Ingredients: 1 cup sifted pastry flour
⅓ tsp. salt
⅓ cup shortening
3 tbsps. ice water

Method: 1. Mix flour and salt; cut shortening into flour mixture.
2. Sprinkle with water and toss with fork to moisten flour mixture.
3. Pat dough lightly together to form a ball; divide into 12 equal portions.
4. Roll out each portion on lightly floured board.
5. Line tart shell pans with pastry; bake at 400°F about 10 to 15 minutes or until golden.

TART SHELLS (GRAHAM WAFER)

Yield: 6 shells

Exchange 1 tart shell for: 1 Bread Exchange
and 1 Fat Exchange

Ingredients: 24 graham wafers (2″ x 2″) or 1 cup graham wafer crumbs
2 tbsps. melted butter or margarine
1 tsp. artificial liquid sweetener
dash of cinnamon

Method: 1. Crush graham wafers; stir in all other ingredients.
2. Press into 6 tart shells; bake at 325°F about 5 minutes; chill before removing from pan.

LEMON OR ORANGE TARTS

Use Lemon or Orange Whip as filling. See pages 110 and 111.

Exchange 1 tart shell (pastry) and filling for: ½ Bread Exchange
and 1 Fat Exchange
and 1 Calorie Free Food
List A

Exchange 1 tart shell (graham wafer) and filling for:
1 Bread Exchange
and 1 Fat Exchange
and 1 Calorie Free Food
List A

GLAZED FRUIT TARTS

Yield: 8 tarts

Exchange 1 tart shell (pastry) and filling for: ½ Bread Exchange
and 1 Fat Exchange
and ½ Fruit Exchange
and 1 Calorie Poor Food
List B

Exchange 1 tart shell (graham wafer) and filling for:
1 Bread Exchange
and 1 Fat Exchange
and ½ Fruit Exchange
and 1 Calorie Poor Food
List B

Ingredients: 1 tsp. cornstarch
2 tsps. cold water
½ cup juice (drained from canned fruits)
4 Fruit Exchanges (preferably from dietetic canned fruits)
8 baked pastry or graham wafer tart shells. See pages 103 and 104.

Method: 1. Blend cornstarch with cold water.
2. Heat fruit juice to boiling; pour over cornstarch stirring constantly.
3. Continue stirring and cook until mixture clears.
4. Arrange fruit in tart shells.
5. Pour 1 tbsp. of sauce over fruit; cool.

PUMPKIN TARTS

Yield: 8 tarts

Exchange filling for 1 tart shell for: ½ Fruit Exchange

Exchange 1 tart shell (pastry) and filling for: ½ Bread Exchange
and 1 Fat Exchange
and ½ Fruit Exchange

Exchange 1 tart shell (graham wafer) and filling for:
1 Bread Exchange
and 1 Fat Exchange
and ½ Fruit Exchange

Ingredients: 1 cup canned pumpkin
¼ tsp. salt
½ tsp. pumpkin pie spice
1 tbsp. fancy molasses
1 tbsp. artificial liquid sweetener
1 envelope vanilla, butterscotch or caramel dietetic pudding powder
½ cup whole milk
8 baked pastry or graham wafer tart shells. See pages 103 and 104.

Method: 1. Mix the first four ingredients together and heat.
2. Add artificial liquid sweetener and pudding powder to milk; stir in the pumpkin mixture.
3. Bring mixture to the boil, stirring constantly.
4. Spoon into tart shells; cool.

ORANGE PINEAPPLE CHARLOTTE

Yield: 6 servings

Exchange 1 serving for: 1 Fruit Exchange
and 1 Fat Exchange

Ingredients: 2 tbsps. or 2 envelopes unflavoured gelatin
⅓ cup cold water
½ cup boiling water
1½ cups orange juice (unsweetened)
1 cup pineapple juice (unsweetened)
2 tsps. artificial liquid sweetener
2 egg whites
⅛ tsp. salt
⅓ cup whipping cream

Method: 1. Soften gelatin in cold water.
2. Add boiling water and stir until dissolved.
3. Add orange juice, pineapple juice and artificial liquid sweetener; mix well.
4. Chill until partially set; whip until frothy.
5. Beat egg whites and salt until stiff; beat whipping cream until stiff.
6. Fold egg whites and whipped cream into the gelatin mixture.
7. Spoon into serving dishes; chill.

FESTIVAL FRUIT

Yield: 4 servings

Exchange 1 serving for: 1 Fruit Exchange
and ½ Bread Exchange

Ingredients: 1 tbsp. or 2 envelopes artificially sweetened strawberry or orange jelly powder
pinch of cloves, cinnamon and nutmeg
1 cup boiling water
4 canned, dietetic plums (chopped fine)
4 tbsps. raisins (chopped fine)
¼ cup Grapenuts

Method: 1. Mix jelly powder with cloves, cinnamon and nutmeg; dissolve in boiling water.
2. Chill until partially set; add all other ingredients; mix well.
3. Pile into serving dishes; chill.

Note: May be unmoulded for serving if desired.

ICE CREAM JELLY BAVARIAN

Yield: 6 servings

Exchange 1 serving for: 1 Fruit Exchange
and 1 Fat Exchange

Ingredients: 2 tbsps. or 4 envelopes artificially sweetened jelly powder
(orange, strawberry, lime, etc.)
2 cups boiling water
1 pint brick ice cream (or 6 ice cream rolls)

Method: 1. Dissolve the jelly powder in boiling water.
2. Allow to cool slightly.
3. Remove ice cream from freezer and leave at room temperature for 5 minutes; cut into small pieces for easier handling.
4. Using a rotary beater or an electric mixer at slow speed, add ice cream to jelly, one piece at a time, mixing until ice cream is melted.
5. Pour into moulds or serving dishes; chill.

Note: May be unmoulded for serving, if desired.

TAPIOCA PUDDING

Yield: 6 servings

Exchange 1 serving for: 1 Fruit Exchange
and 1 Meat Exchange

Ingredients: 2 eggs, separated
2½ cups whole milk
3 tbsps. 'quick cooking' tapioca
¼ tsp. salt
1 tsp. vanilla
1 tsp. artificial liquid sweetener

Method: 1. Beat egg yolks with a small amount of the milk in a saucepan.
2. Add remaining milk, tapioca and salt.
3. Cook, stirring constantly until the mixture comes to a full boil.
4. Add vanilla and artificial liquid sweetener.
5. Beat egg whites until they stand in soft peaks.
6. Pour tapioca mixture very slowly over beaten egg whites, stirring rapidly to blend.
7. Pile into serving dishes; chill.

RICE-RAISIN CUSTARD PUDDING

Yield: 6 servings

Exchange 1 serving for: 1 Fruit Exchange
and 1 Meat Exchange

Ingredients: 3 eggs
2 cups whole milk
½ tsp. salt
2 tsps. artificial liquid sweetener
1 tsp. vanilla
⅔ cup cooked rice
2 tbsps. raisins
nutmeg

Method: 1. Beat eggs.
2. Add all other ingredients; mix.
3. Pour into custard cups; sprinkle with nutmeg.
4. Set cups in a shallow pan of hot water.
5. Bake at 325°F about 30 minutes or until set.

BREAD PUDDING

Yield: 6 servings

Exchange 1 serving for: 1 Milk Exchange
and ½ Bread Exchange

Ingredients: 2 slices of white bread
2½ cups whole milk
1 egg
pinch of salt
2 tsps. artificial liquid sweetener
1 tsp. vanilla
3 tbsps. raisins
nutmeg

Method: 1. Cube bread and soak in milk until soft; beat until smooth.
2. Beat egg; add with all other ingredients to the bread-milk mixture; mix thoroughly.
3. Pour into baking dishes; sprinkle with nutmeg.
4. Set dishes in a shallow pan of hot water.
5. Bake at 325°F about 30 minutes or until set.

PLUM PUDDING

Yield: 6 servings
Exchange 1 serving for: 1 Fruit Exchange
and 2 Fat Exchanges

Ingredients: ⅔ cup grated raw carrot
⅓ cup raisins
3 tbsps. suet
½ cup flour
3 tbsps. grated lemon rind
1 tbsp. artificial liquid sweetener
¾ tsp. allspice
¾ tsp. nutmeg
¾ tsp. cinnamon
¾ tsp. vanilla
f.g. salt
3 egg yolks

Method: 1. Combine all ingredients; mix well.
2. Divide into 6 individual moulds; steam 30 to 40 minutes.
3. Serve hot with sauce of choice. See pages 111 or 112.

DUTCH APPLE CAKE

Yield: 8 servings
Exchange 1 serving for: 1 Fruit Exchange
and 1 Bread Exchange
and 1 Fat Exchange

Ingredients: 2 medium apples
1½ cups flour
½ tsp. salt
1 tbsp. baking powder
2 tbsps. shortening
¼ cup skim milk
¼ cup water
1 tbsp. artificial liquid sweetener
1 tbsp. cinnamon

Method: 1. Wash, pare, core and slice apples.
2. Sift flour, salt, and baking powder; cut shortening into flour mixture.
3. Add water and sweetener to milk; add to flour mixture.
4. Mix well; knead dough about 5 times.
5. Spread in greased loaf pan (4″ x 8″); scatter apples on top, pushing sharp edges into dough.
6. Sprinkle with cinnamon.
7. Bake at 350°F about 30 minutes; serve hot with lemon sauce. See page 111.

FRUIT SHORTCAKE

Fruit shortcake consists of a cake or biscuit base and fresh or unsweetened frozen fruit.

For cake base use Orange Cake recipe. See page 114.

Exchange 1 serving of Cake and fruit for: 1 Bread Exchange
and 1½ Fat Exchanges
and 1 Fruit Exchange

For biscuit base use Tea Biscuit recipe. See page 126.

Exchange 1 Tea Biscuit and fruit for: 1 Bread Exchange
and 1 Fat Exchange
and 1 Fruit Exchange

CALORIE FREE DESSERTS

Here are two basic recipes which may be used to dress up any of the artificially flavoured jelly powders (lime, raspberry, strawberry, cherry, etc.).

They also make fine toppings for plain desserts or cakes.

LEMON WHIP

Yield: 6 servings

Exchange 1 serving for: 1 Calorie Free Food List A

Ingredients: 1 tbsp. or 2 envelopes artificially sweetened lemon jelly powder
2 cups boiling water
2 egg whites
⅛ tsp. salt
1 tsp. grated lemon rind
1 tbsp. lemon juice

Method: 1. Dissolve jelly powder in boiling water.
2. Chill until partially set; whip until frothy.
3. Beat egg whites and salt until stiff; whip these ingredients into the gelatin mixture until the jelly holds its shape.
4. Fold in grated lemon rind and lemon juice.
5. Pile into serving dishes; chill.

ORANGE WHIP

Yield: 6 servings

Exchange 1 serving for: 1 Calorie Free Food List A

Ingredients: 1 tbsp. or 2 envelopes artificially sweetened orange jelly
powder
1 cup boiling water
1 cup artificially sweetened ginger ale
2 egg whites
⅛ tsp. salt

Method: 1. Dissolve jelly powder in boiling water.
2. Add ginger ale; mix well.
3. Chill until partially set; whip until frothy.
4. Beat egg whites and salt until stiff; whip these ingredients into gelatin mixture until jelly holds its shape.
5. Pile into serving dishes; chill.

GARNISHES AND SAUCES FOR DESSERTS

These give the finishing touch and should be as attractive as possible. Why not try: —

— Fresh, unsweetened or dietetic canned fruit (counted as a Fruit Exchange) to make a colourful addition to any of the Milk Exchange Desserts.

— Soft Custard (⅓ cup for ½ Milk Exchange and ½ Fat Exchange) with a baked apple or prune whip. See page 97.

— Lemon and Orange Whips (Calorie Free Food List A). See page 110 and above.

— Whipped Cream (1 tbsp. for 1 Fat Exchange) as a pleasing garnish for a jellied fruit or chocolate pudding. See pages 96 and 99.

— For additional suggestions see page 97.

LEMON SAUCE

Yield: 1 cup

Exchange 2 tbsps. sauce for: 1 Calorie Poor Food List B

Ingredients: 1 tbsp. cornstarch
⅛ tsp. salt
2 tbsps. cold water
1 cup boiling water
1 tsp. artificial liquid sweetener
2 tbsps. lemon juice
grated rind of one lemon
⅛ tsp. nutmeg
2 tsps. butter or margarine

Method: 1. Combine cornstarch and salt and blend with cold water.
2. Add boiling water gradually, stirring constantly.
3. Continue stirring and cook until mixture clears.
4. Add remaining ingredients; mix well; serve warm.

ORANGE SAUCE

Yield: 1 cup

Exchange 2 tbsps. sauce for: 1 Calorie Poor Food List B

Ingredients: 4 tsps. cornstarch
⅛ tsp. salt
¼ cup cold water
1 tsp. artificial liquid sweetener
¼ tsp. grated orange rind
¾ cup boiling water
4 tbsps. orange juice
few drops lemon juice

Method: 1. Combine cornstarch and salt and blend with cold water; add artificial liquid sweetener and orange rind.
2. Add boiling water gradually, stirring constantly.
3. Continue stirring and cook until mixture clears.
4. Add orange and lemon juices; mix well.
5. Serve warm.

CHOCOLATE SAUCE

Yield: 1 cup

Exchange 1 tbsp. sauce for: 1 Calorie Poor Food List B

Ingredients: 2 tbsps. cocoa
2 tsps. cornstarch
⅛ tsp. salt
1 tbsp. melted butter or margarine
1 cup skim milk
2 tsps. artificial liquid sweetener
½ tsp. vanilla

Method: 1. Combine cocoa, cornstarch and salt and blend with melted butter or margarine until smooth.
2. Add milk and artificial liquid sweetener; cook, stirring constantly until slightly thickened, and there is no taste of raw starch.
3. Stir in vanilla.
4. Set pan in cold water and stir until completely cool. Sauce thickens as it cools.

CAKES, COOKIES AND QUICK BREADS

An anniversary celebration? Company for dinner? Or just a family gathering? Here's something for every occasion.

To add a special touch, try any of the following recipes. But take a tip from us. **FOLLOW THE RECIPES EXACTLY** and **REMEMBER THAT ALL MEASUREMENTS ARE LEVEL.**

CHOCOLATE or WHITE CAKE MIX (9½ oz. pkg.)

Yield: 20 servings, by cutting cake 4 x 5

Exchange 1 serving for: 1 Bread Exchange
and 1 Fat Exchange

Method: 1. Follow directions on package.
2. Bake in 8″ square pan.

Variations:

1) Bake cake in loaf pan. Cut into 20 slices.

Exchange 1 slice for: 1 Bread Exchange
and 1 Fat Exchange

2) Preheat oven to 375°F. Divide cake batter evenly into 20 paper-cup-lined muffin tins. Bake 15 to 20 minutes.

Exchange 1 cup cake for: 1 Bread Exchange
and 1 Fat Exchange

3) Preheat oven to 350°F. To cake mix, add 1 egg and ¼ cup vegetable oil. Blend well. Drop batter by teaspoonful onto ungreased cookie sheet to make 7 doz. cookies. Bake 10 to 15 minutes or until lightly browned.

Exchange 4 cookies for: 1 Bread Exchange
and 1 Fat Exchange

ANGEL FOOD CAKE MIX (15 oz. pkg.)

Yield: 20 servings

Exchange 1 serving for: 1 Bread Exchange

Method: 1. Follow directions on package.
2. Bake in tube pan.

ORANGE CAKE

Yield: 10 servings

Exchange 1 serving for: 1 Bread Exchange
and 1½ Fat Exchanges

Ingredients: 1 cup sifted cake flour
1½ tsps. baking powder
½ tsp. salt
¼ cup vegetable oil
3 egg yolks
½ cup unsweetened frozen orange juice concentrate
3 tsps. liquid artificial sweetener
3 egg whites
¼ tsp. cream of tartar
1 tsp. grated orange rind

Method: 1. Preheat oven to 325°F.

2. Sift together thoroughly, several times, flour, baking powder and salt.

3. Make a "well" in the mixture.

4. Add in order: vegetable oil, unbeaten egg yolks, orange juice concentrate and sweetener; beat until smooth.

5. Add cream of tartar to egg whites and beat until very stiff.

6. Fold stiffly beaten egg whites and grated orange rind into flour mixture.

7. Pour into 9" tube pan, lined with waxed paper (on bottom) and dusted with flour.

8. Bake 35 minutes.

9. Remove from oven; invert so that tube rests on an inverted glass tumbler; let cool for 20 minutes; slide knife around edge to loosen; turn onto plate.

ORANGE SPONGE CAKE

Yield: 10 servings

Exchange 1 serving for: ½ Bread Exchange
and ½ Fruit Exchange
and ½ Fat Exchange

Ingredients: 1 cup sifted cake or pastry flour
½ tsp. salt
½ cup unsweetened frozen orange juice concentrate
¼ cup corn oil, or other vegetable oil
1 tsp. grated orange rind
3 tsps. liquid artificial sweetener
2 tbsps. water
6 egg whites
1½ tsps. baking powder
¼ tsp. cream of tartar

Method: 1. Preheat oven to 325°F.

2. Sift flour and salt together.

3. In another bowl combine orange juice, corn oil, grated peel, sweetener and water.

4. Add this mixture to the flour and beat with a whisk until smooth (about 30 seconds).

5. In a third bowl beat egg whites, baking powder and cream of tartar until very stiff, but not dry.

6. Gently FOLD egg whites into batter until mixed thoroughly.

7. Spoon into 7″ tube pan, lined with waxed paper (on bottom) and dusted with flour.

8. Bake 35 minutes.

9. Remove from oven; invert so that tube rests on an inverted glass tumbler; let cool for 20 minutes; slide knife around edge to loosen, and turn onto plate.

CUP CAKES

Yield: 16 cup cakes

Exchange 1 cup cake for: 1 Bread Exchange
and 1 Fat Exchange

Ingredients: ½ cup margarine
⅔ cup sugar
½ tsp. vanilla
2 eggs
1½ cups unsifted cake flour
1¼ tsps. baking powder
¼ tsp. salt
⅓ cup 2% milk

Method: 1. Preheat oven to 375°F.
2. Cream margarine; add sugar gradually and beat until light and fluffy.
3. Add vanilla, then eggs one at a time, beating well after each addition.
4. Mix cake flour, baking powder and salt; add alternately with milk to creamed mixture, beating after each addition until smooth.
5. Half-fill 16 paper-cup-lined muffin tins with batter.
6. Bake 20 to 25 minutes.
7. Cool slightly; then immediately remove from tins to rack to cool.

Variations: 1. Serve warm with fruit allowance as an Upside-Down Pudding.
2. Ice cup cakes with a topping. See pages 129 and 130.

BROWNIES

Yield: 16 squares, 2″ x 2″

Exchange 1 square for: 1 Fruit Exchange
and 1 Fat Exchange

Ingredients: 3 oz. semi-sweet chocolate (pieces or squares)
2 cups fine graham cracker crumbs
½ cup chopped walnuts
2 tsps. liquid artificial sweetener
¼ tsp. salt
1 cup skim milk

116

Method: 1. Preheat oven to 350°F.

2. Melt chocolate in top of double boiler, over boiling water.

3. Combine remainder of ingredients; add melted chocolate and stir until blended.

4. Turn into slightly greased pan 8″ x 8″ x 2″.

5. Bake 30 minutes.

6. While warm, cut into 16 equal squares by dividing pan 4 x 4; cool before removing from pan.

FRUIT AND NUT COOKIES

Yield: 18 cookies

Exchange 2 cookies for: 1 Fruit Exchange
and 1 Fat Exchange

Exchange 3 cookies for: 1 Bread Exchange
and 1½ Fat Exchanges

Ingredients: 3 tbsps. shortening
3 tbsps. chopped dates
4 tbsps. chopped walnuts
3 tbsps. raisins
¼ cup all purpose flour
¼ tsp. baking soda
1 egg
¼ tsp. liquid artificial sweetener

Method: 1. Preheat oven to 375°F.

2. Cream shortening until soft.

3. Chop dates and nuts; place raisins in hot water to soften.

4. Sift flour and soda together; add dates, nuts and drained raisins.

5. Beat egg until foamy; add sweetener and creamed shortening.

6. Add flour mixture, in thirds, stirring just enough to combine ingredients.

7. Drop, by teaspoonful, on greased cookie sheet, dividing batter into 18 cookies.

8. Bake 12 to 15 minutes, until lightly browned. (A toothpick comes out clean.)

9. Remove from pan while hot.

PEANUT BUTTER COOKIES

Yield: 30 cookies

Exchange 3 cookies for: 1 Bread Exchange
and 2 Fat Exchanges

Ingredients: 2 tbsps. shortening
6 tbsps. peanut butter
¼ cup sugar
3 tbsps. water
2 eggs
½ tsp. vanilla
1¼ cups all purpose flour
½ tsp. baking soda
½ tsp. baking powder
¼ tsp. salt

Method:
1. Preheat oven to 375°F.
2. Grease cookie sheets.
3. Cream shortening and peanut butter until light and fluffy.
4. Beat in sugar, water, eggs and vanilla. BATTER MAY CURDLE.
5. Sift together flour, baking soda, baking powder and salt.
6. Stir flour mixture into shortening mixture until smooth.
7. Drop dough, by tablespoonful, onto cookie sheets; flatten each with a fork dipped in cold water.
8. Bake 10 to 12 minutes, until golden brown around edges.
9. Remove from sheets while hot.

OATMEAL COOKIES

Yield: 48 cookies

Exchange 1 cookie for: 1 Bread Exchange

Ingredients: ⅓ cup sifted, all purpose flour
1 tsp. baking powder
⅛ tsp. baking soda
¼ tsp. salt
½ cup molasses
1 egg
1 tbsp. 2% milk
¼ cup butter or margarine melted
1¼ cups quick-cooking oatmeal

Method: 1. Preheat oven to 375°F.
   2. Sift together flour, baking powder, baking soda and salt.
   3. Combine molasses, slightly beaten egg, milk and melted butter or margarine; mix well.
   4. Add flour mixture and oatmeal gradually.
   5. Drop, by teaspoonful, onto greased cookie sheets, leaving 2″ between each.
   6. Bake 12 to 15 minutes.

Variation: ¼ cup raisins may be added, without altering the exchange value for each cookie.

FRUIT BALLS

Yield: 18 fruit balls

Exchange 1 fruit ball for: ½ Fruit Exchange
 and ½ Fat Exchange

Ingredients: ½ cup artificially sweetened canned red cherries
 ½ cup chopped dates
 ½ cup chopped walnuts

Method: 1. Drain cherries and reserve juice.
   2. Mix fruit and nuts.
   3. Add just enough cherry juice to hold mixture together.
   4. Form into balls, allowing 1½ tbsps. for each.
   5. Chill on waxed-paper-lined tray or rack.

Variations: Each fruit ball may be rolled in:
   1. Shredded coconut, allowing 1 tsp. per ball.
   2. Finely chopped walnuts, allowing 1 tsp. per ball.
   3. Artificially sweetened vanilla pudding powder.

Note: In these amounts, none of these additions will appreciably change the food value of the fruit balls.

SHORTBREAD

Yield: 60 cookies

Exchange 1 cookie for: ½ Fruit Exchange
and ½ Fat Exchange

Ingredients: 1 cup butter or margarine
⅔ cup brown sugar, sifted
1 egg yolk
2⅔ cups sifted all purpose flour

Method: 1. Cream butter or margarine and sugar together.
2. Add slightly beaten egg yolk.
3. Add flour gradually; mix well.
4. Chill dough.
5. Preheat oven to 325°F.
6. Roll chilled dough out to ⅓″ thickness.
7. Cut into 60 cookies (using 2″ cookie cutter).
8. Place cookies on ungreased cookie sheet and bake for 30 minutes, (until lightly browned).
9. Store in cool place.

CHEESE MOONS

Yield: 32 cookies

Exchange 1 cookie for: ½ Fruit Exchange
and 2 Fat Exchanges

Ingredients: ½ lb. (1 cup) butter or margarine
½ lb. white cream cheese
2 cups sifted pastry flour
artificially sweetened jam spread

Method: 1. Preheat oven to 350°F-375°F.
2. Cream butter or margarine and cheese together.
3. Add flour slowly, reserving enough to flour the baking board.
4. When dough becomes stiff, turn it on to floured board; knead in remaining flour with your hands.
5. Roll thin; cut into 32 cookies, using 2½″ round cutter.
6. Place ½ to 1 tsp. jam spread on half of each cookie.
7. Fold unspread side over and press edges together.
8. Bake until golden brown (25 to 30 minutes).

COCONUT FLUFFS

Yield: 12 fluffs

Exchange 1 fluff for: 1 Fat Exchange

Ingredients: 6 tbsps. white cream cheese
1⅛ tsps. liquid artificial sweetener
1 tsp. grated orange and/or lemon rind
1 tsp. chopped almonds or walnuts
¼ cup shredded coconut

Method: 1. Toast coconut in 325°F oven until lightly brown.
2. With spoon, mix cheese and sweetener until light and fluffy.
3. Add grated rind and nuts; mix thoroughly.
4. Form into 12 balls and roll each in toasted coconut.
5. Refrigerate until serving time.

Variation: Tint coconut with food colouring instead of toasting it.

MERINGUES

Yield: 18 cookies

Exchange 1 cookie for: ½ Bread Exchange

Ingredients: 2 egg whites
½ tsp. vanilla
½ tsp. cream of tartar
¼ tsp. salt
⅓ cup sugar
artificially sweetened jam spread (optional)

Method: 1. Preheat oven to 225°F.
2. Beat egg whites until foamy; add vanilla, cream of tartar and salt, and beat slightly.
3. Gradually add sugar, beating thoroughly until stiff peaks are formed.
4. Drop 18 small mounds (with a teaspoon) onto baking sheet lined with brown paper, allowing 2″ between each.
5. Hollow the centre of each to form shallow shells.
6. Bake 1 hour, or until meringues are dry.
7. Cool; fill each shell with 1 tsp. of jam spread.

Variation: Tint with food colouring, as desired.

PRESSED COOKIES

Yield: 36 cookies

Exchange 1 cookie for: ½ Bread Exchange
and 2 Fat Exchanges

Ingredients: 2 cups sifted cake flour
¼ tsp. salt
¼ cup butter or margarine
½ cup shortening
½ cup sugar
1 egg yolk
½ tsp. almond extract

Method: 1. Preheat oven to 375°F.
2. Sift flour and remeasure; add salt and sift again.
3. Cream shortening and butter or margarine; gradually add sugar and beat until light.
4. Add egg yolk and almond extract; blend thoroughly.
5. Combine with dry ingredients; mix to a smooth dough.
6. Force through cookie press onto greased cookie sheet. If dough is too soft to hold its shape when pressed, store in refrigerator until firm.
7. Bake until lightly browned (8 to 10 minutes).

CINNAMON SPICE COOKIES

Yield: 30 cookies

Exchange 3 cookies for: 1 Bread Exchange
and ½ Fat Exchange

Ingredients: 5 tbsps. butter or margarine
⅓ cup sugar
1 cup sifted all purpose flour
½ tsp. baking powder
1 tsp. cinnamon
pinch of salt
1 tsp. vanilla
1½ tbsps. 2% milk **or** fruit juice **or** coffee

Method: 1. Preheat oven to 375°F.
2. Cream butter or margarine until light and fluffy.
3. Blend in sugar, flour, baking powder, cinnamon and salt.
4. Combine vanilla and milk (or other liquid); stir into flour mixture and blend thoroughly. **DOUGH MAY BE CRUMBLY.**
5. Shape dough into 30 balls of equal size, and place on cookie sheet.
6. Flatten each ball with a fork dipped in cold water.
7. Bake until cookies are lightly browned (10 to 15 minutes).

BANANA MUFFINS

Yield: 6 muffins

Exchange 1 muffin for: 1 Bread Exchange
and 1 Fat Exchange

Ingredients: ¾ cup sifted pastry flour
1 tsp. baking powder
⅛ tsp. baking soda
⅛ tsp. salt
½ cup mashed bananas
⅜ tsp. liquid artificial sweetener
1 tbsp. skim milk
⅛ tsp. vanilla
2 tbsps. plus 2 tsps. corn oil, or other vegetable oil
1 egg white

Method:
1. Preheat oven to 350°F.
2. Sift together dry ingredients.
3. In another bowl, beat mashed bananas with mixer until smooth.
4. With mixer, beat in sweetener, milk, vanilla and corn oil until well blended.
5. In third bowl, beat egg white well.
6. Fold liquid ingredients and egg white into dry ingredients. Mix just until blended (batter will appear lumpy). **DO NOT OVERMIX.**
7. Line muffin tins with six paper baking cups.
8. Divide batter evenly into cups.
9. Bake 15 to 20 minutes.

BRAN MUFFINS

Yield: 9 muffins

Exchange 1 muffin for: 1 Bread Exchange

Ingredients: ½ cup all purpose flour
½ tsp. baking soda
½ tsp. salt
1 cup prepared bran cereal
1 egg
¼ cup molasses
⅝ cup 2% milk

Method:
1. Preheat oven to 375°F.
2. Sift together flour, soda and salt.
3. Add bran, beaten egg and molasses.
4. Add milk; stir just until dry ingredients are moistened.
5. Divide mixture equally into 9 lightly greased muffin tins.
6. Bake 20 minutes.

BLUEBERRY MUFFINS

Yield: 12 muffins

Exchange 1 muffin for: 1 Bread Exchange
and 1 Fat Exchange

Ingredients: 2 cups sifted all purpose flour
2½ tsps. baking powder
1 tsp. salt
½ cup blueberries, fresh or frozen
1 egg
2 tsps. liquid artificial sweetener
1 cup 2% milk
2 tbsps. melted butter or margarine

Method: 1. Preheat oven to 375°F.
2. Sift flour again with baking powder and salt.
3. Add blueberries to flour mixture; mix until well coated.
4. Add slightly beaten egg, sweetener, milk and melted butter or margarine; mix until blended.
5. Divide mixture evenly into 12 lightly greased muffin tins.
6. Bake 20 to 30 minutes.

Variation: Replace blueberries with another fruit, e.g. fresh cherries or pineapple.

CORNMEAL MUFFINS

Yield: 15 muffins

Exchange 1 muffin for: 1 Bread Exchange
and 1 Fat Exchange

Ingredients: 5 tbsps. corn oil, or other vegetable oil
2 tsps. liquid artificial sweetener
¼ cup water
4 egg whites
1¼ cups cornmeal
¾ cup all purpose flour
2½ tsps. baking powder
¾ tsp. salt
¾ cup skim milk

Method: 1. Preheat oven to 400°F. and line 15 muffin tins with paper baking cups.
2. Beat together corn oil, sweetener, water and egg whites.
3. Stir in cornmeal.
4. Sift together remaining dry ingredients.
5. GENTLY FOLD into cornmeal mixture, in following order: one-third sifted dry ingredients; one-half skim milk; another third of dry ingredients; remaining milk; remaining dry ingredients.
6. Divide evenly into 15 muffin tins.
7. Bake until golden brown (20 to 25 minutes).

ORANGE NUT BREAD

Yield: 1 loaf (9" x 5" x 3") or 12 slices

Exchange 1 slice for: 1 Bread Exchange
and 1 Fat Exchange

Ingredients: 2 cups sifted all purpose flour
1½ tsps. baking powder
½ tsp. baking soda
¼ tsp. salt
1 egg
⅓ cup skim milk
3 tsps. liquid artificial sweetener
2 tbsps. melted butter or margarine
½ cup artificially sweetened orange fruit spread
¼ cup chopped walnuts or pecans.

Method: 1. Preheat oven to 350°F.
2. Combine and sift dry ingredients.
3. Beat egg; add milk and sweetener; add to flour mixture.
4. Stir only until all flour is moistened; then gradually stir in melted butter or margarine.
5. Fold in fruit spread and nuts, mixing as little as possible.
6. Transfer to lightly greased loaf pan (9" x 5" x 3").
7. Bake for 1 hour and 40 minutes, or until loaf springs back when pressed lightly with finger.
8. Cool before slicing.

BANANA LOAF

Yield: 1 loaf (8″ x 4″ x 3″) or 15 slices

Exchange 1 slice for: 1 Bread Exchange
and 1 Fat Exchange

Ingredients: 1¾ cups sifted cake flour
2 tsps. baking powder
¼ tsp. baking soda
½ tsp. salt
4 tbsps. melted shortening
2 eggs, well beaten
3 tsps. liquid artificial sweetener
1 tsp. vanilla
⅔ cup mashed bananas (2 medium bananas)

Method: 1. Preheat oven to 350°F.

2. Sift together dry ingredients.

3. Combine shortening, eggs, sweetener and vanilla.

4. Add to flour mixture and stir only until flour is moistened.

5. Fold in mashed bananas.

6. Place in greased loaf pan (8″ x 4″ x 3″).

7. Bake 60 to 70 minutes.

TEA BISCUITS

Yield: 10 biscuits

Exchange 1 biscuit for: 1 Bread Exchange
and 1 Fat Exchange

Ingredients: 2 cups sifted all purpose flour
3 tsps. baking powder
½ tsp. salt
4 tbsps. shortening
¾ cup skim milk

Method: 1. Preheat oven to 450°F.

2. Sift together flour, baking powder and salt.

3. Cut in shortening with a knife, until very fine.

4. Add milk; stir lightly with a fork until mixed.

5. Turn onto slightly floured board; knead lightly, and roll ½″ thick.

6. Cut, with a knife, into 10 biscuits of equal size.

7. Place on slightly greased pan.

8. Bake 12 to 15 minutes.

Variations: Serve with fruit allowance as an Upside-Down pudding, or as shortcake.

WAFFLES

Yield: 30 waffles

Exchange 1 waffle (1 tbsp. mixture) for: ½ Bread Exchange

Ingredients: 2 cups sifted all purpose flour
3 tsps. baking powder
½ tsp. salt
2 tsps. sugar
2 egg yolks
1⅔ cups skim milk
1½ tbsps. melted butter or margarine
2 egg whites

Method: 1. Sift dry ingredients together.

2. Gradually add beaten egg yolks, milk and butter or margarine; fold in stiffly beaten egg whites.

3. Heat waffle iron.

4. Pour 1 tbsp. mixture into each section, near the centre.

5. Cook until crisp and brown.

6. Serve at once, with 1 tsp. artificially sweetened jam spread if desired.

FRENCH PANCAKES (Crêpes)

Yield: 32 crêpes, each 2" diameter

Exchange 3 crêpes for: 1 Bread Exchange
and 1 Fat Exchange

Ingredients: ¾ cup all purpose flour
f.g. salt
2 eggs
3 tbsps. butter or margarine
¾ tsp. vanilla
½ tsp. grated orange rind
½ tsp. grated lemon rind
⅜ tsp. liquid artificial sweetener
¾ cup 2% milk

Method:
1. Sift flour and salt together.
2. Add all other ingredients except milk; beat until perfectly smooth (2 to 3 minutes).
3. Add milk and mix thoroughly; let batter stand half an hour.
4. In a frying pan melt about ½ tsp. butter or margarine to grease the bottom.
5. Pour in enough batter to make crêpes approximately 2" in diameter.
6. Cook 1 minute; turn and cook another minute.
7. Continue until all batter is used.

FROSTINGS AND TOPPINGS

To add a touch of glamour to cakes, cup cakes and some desserts!

SKIM MILK TOPPING

Yield: 2½ cups

Exchange 1 tbsp. topping for: 1 Calorie Free Food List A

Ingredients: ½ cup skim milk powder
⅓ cup ice water
1 tbsp. lemon juice
1⅛ tsps. liquid artificial sweetener

Method: 1. Add skim milk powder to ice water in a mixing bowl.
2. Beat with electric mixer on high speed until mixture stands in soft peaks.
3. Add lemon juice; continue beating until quite firm.
4. Fold in sweetener and chill.

Variations: 1. Spicy Topping: add 1 tsp. nutmeg and ½ tsp. cinnamon while whipping.
2. Mocha Topping: add 1 tsp. instant coffee while whipping.
3. Tinted Topping: add few drops food colouring while whipping.
4. Mint Topping: add ½ tsp. mint flavouring and few drops green food colouring while whipping.

CHOCOLATE FROSTING

Yield: 8 tbsps. frosting, or 8 servings

Exchange 1 tbsp. frosting for: 1 Calorie Poor Food List B

Ingredients: 1 oz. unsweetened chocolate
6 tbsps. evaporated milk
½ tsp. vanilla
1⅛ tsps. liquid artificial sweetener

Method: 1. Melt chocolate over hot water.
2. Stir in evaporated milk and mix well.
3. Cook until it thickens (2 or 3 minutes).
4. Remove from heat; stir in vanilla and sweetener. If too thick, thin down with water to spreading consistency.

FRUIT FROSTING

Yield: 4 tbsps. frosting, or 4 servings

Exchange 1 tbsp. frosting for: 1 Fat Exchange

Ingredients: 4 tbsps. white cream cheese
2 tsps. artificially sweetened jam spread

Method: 1. Soften cream cheese at room temperature (½ hour).
2. Add jam spread and beat vigorously using rotary beater or electric mixer.

Variations: 1. Replace jam spread with ½ tsp. of instant coffee mixed with 2 tsps. hot water and ⅛ tsp. liquid artificial sweetener.
2. To softened cheese add 1 tbsp. milk, ⅛ tsp. liquid artificial sweetener and 1 or 2 drops vanilla; beat vigorously.
3. Add choice of food colourings to plain frosting.
4. Add ¼ tsp. grated lemon or orange rind to plain frosting.

WHIPPED CREAM

Exchange 1 rounded tbsp. whipped cream, plain or with any of the following additions for: 1 Fat Exchange

Variations: 1. Add your choice of food colourings.
2. Add a drop of liquid artificial sweetener and a drop of vanilla to each tbsp. of whipped cream.
3. Add ¼ tsp. instant coffee to ¼ cup whipped cream, **before beating.**

FOR THE GOURMET

" . . . Exalt your effort; stimulate, intensify, indeed magnify the flavor. Your appreciation and appetite will increase. You will add to the pleasure of your guests."

Alice B. Toklas "Aromas and Flavors"

This is exactly what you will do as you prepare and enjoy the special recipes we have selected for this very special Gourmet Section. No additional cooking skills are necessary to prepare any of these. Some recipes contain wine; however, during cooking, almost all the alcohol evaporates and leaves a typical aroma and a delicious flavour. Since the use of wine is optional, many of the recipes suggest an alternate ingredient. You will note that no alternate has been suggested in a few recipes where the wine gives the dish its particular character, e.g. Peaches Flambé. Remember that if wine is used as called for, its caloric value is small and does not appreciably affect the total value of the recipe.

PATE DE FOIE GRAS

Yield: 10 to 12 servings
Exchange 1 tablespoon for: ½ Meat Exchange
Ingredients: 1 lb. calves or beef liver
1 medium onion
1 large stalk celery
2 tbsps. lemon juice
salt and pepper to taste
Method: 1. Boil liver in water until tender.
2. Remove skin, fibre and tubes.
3. Grind in food chopper with onion and celery.
4. Blend with lemon juice until smooth.
5. Add salt and pepper to taste.
6. Form into a large mound and chill thoroughly.

MARINATED MUSHROOMS

Yield: 6 servings

Exchange 1 serving for: ½ Fat Exchange

Ingredients: 1½ lbs. tiny button mushrooms
1 cup dry white wine **or** 1 cup chicken stock. See page 8.
¼ cup olive oil
1 clove garlic (impaled with toothpick for easy removal)
juice of 1 lemon
½ tsp. each dried rosemary, tarragon and oregano
½ small bay leaf
salt and freshly ground pepper to taste
parsley, chopped, as garnish (optional)

Method: 1. Cut stems from mushrooms level with caps and reserve for other uses.
2. Add remaining ingredients (except garnish) to mushroom caps in a saucepan; bring to a boil and simmer for 8 to 10 minutes.
3. Cool, discard garlic, and chill slightly, but not long enough for oil to congeal.
4. Drain and serve garnished with chopped parsley.

Note: The smallest, freshest mushrooms should be used.

SHRIMP COCKTAIL

Yield: 4 servings (Cocktails)

Exchange 1 serving (1 Cocktail) for: 1 Meat Exchange
and 1 Vegetable Exchange List 2B

First, make **Cocktail Sauce** (makes about ½ cup)

Ingredients: 3 oz. or 6 tbsps. chili sauce
1½ tbsps. lemon juice
1½ tsps. prepared horseradish
1 tsp. Worcestershire sauce
¼ tsp. grated onion
few drops Tabasco sauce

Method: 1. Combine all ingredients; salt to taste.
2. Chill.

Just before serving time, assemble **Cocktails:**

Ingredients: 4 crisp lettuce leaves
16 medium shrimps, cooked, peeled, deveined and chilled
½ cup **Cocktail Sauce**
½ lemon, sliced thinly
parsley

Method: 1. Place one leaf lettuce and 4 shrimps in each of 4 cocktail glasses.

2. Cover each with 2 tbsps. **Cocktail Sauce.**

3. Garnish with lemon slices and parsley.

Variation: Substitute 1 cup cooked, flaked crab or lobster meat for shrimps. Divide equally into 4 servings.

VICHYSSOISE

Yield: 4 servings

Exchange 1 serving for: 1 Milk Exchange
and 1 Vegetable Exchange List 2B

Ingredients: ½ onion, finely grated (about 2 tsps. after grating)
1 chicken bouillon cube
¾ cup boiling water
f.g. salt
1 cup whole milk
½ cup instant potato flakes
½ cup 10% cream, chilled
chives or parsley, finely chopped, to garnish

Method: 1. Combine onion, bouillon cube, boiling water and salt in saucepan.

2. Bring to boil; reduce heat; cover and cook gently (about 5 minutes).

3. Remove from heat; add ¼ cup cold milk; quickly stir in instant potato flakes and whip with fork until fluffy.

4. Gradually stir in remainder of milk; heat just to boiling and remove from heat.

5. Cover and chill thoroughly.

6. Just before serving, stir in chilled cream; beat vigorously with fork, or in electric blender, for a few seconds.

7. Serve in 4 chilled consomme cups or glasses packed in ice, if desired; sprinkle each serving with finely chopped chives or parsley.

OYSTER STEW

Yield: 4 servings

Exchange 1 serving for: 2 Meat Exchanges
and 1 Milk Exchange
and 1 Vegetable Exchange List 2A

Ingredients: 2 cups skim milk
12 soda biscuits (2″ size), crumbled
1 tsp. salt
f.g. pepper
4 tsps. butter or margarine
24 oysters plus liquor

Method:
1. Place the first five ingredients in top of double boiler, and heat over boiling water.
2. Drain liquor from oysters, and save liquor.
3. Remove any pieces of shell from oysters.
4. Heat oysters and liquor together slowly until edges of oysters begin to curl.
5. Add heated oysters and liquor slowly to hot milk mixture.
6. Reheat; **do not boil;** serve at once.

CLAM CHOWDER

Yield: 4 servings

Exchange 1 serving for: 2 Meat Exchanges
and 1 Vegetable Exchange List 2A

Ingredients: 1½ cups clams (save clam liquor)
½ cup salt pork, cubed
¼ cup onion, chopped
2 stalks celery, chopped
½ cup raw potato, diced
⅔ cup water
½ cup canned tomatoes
¾ cup tomato juice
2 tsps. parsley, chopped
½ tsp. salt

Method:
1. Chop clams and scald in clam liquor; strain.
2. Fry pork cubes in their own fat until crisp.
3. Add chopped onion and cook until tender.
4. Drain fat from pork and onion.
5. Cook celery and potato in the ⅔ cup water.
6. Add remaining ingredients; simmer 10 to 15 minutes.
7. Serve piping hot; **do not boil**.

SALMON STEAK BAKED IN RED WINE

Yield: 4 servings

Exchange 1 serving for: 3 Meat Exchanges
and 1 Fat Exchange
and 1 Calorie Poor Food List B

Ingredients: 4 tsps. butter or margarine, melted
4 salmon steaks (4 oz. each)
½ tsp. salt and dash pepper
1½ tbsps. shallots (or onions), finely chopped
¼ cup dry red wine (or red wine vinegar)
1 tbsp. freshly squeezed lemon juice
¼ tsp. cornstarch dissolved in 1 tbsp. cold water
7 seedless grapes cut in half (optional)

Method:
1. Preheat oven to 400°F.
2. Grease, with 1 tsp. butter or margarine, a baking dish large enough to hold 4 steaks.
3. Season steaks with salt and pepper and brush with remaining melted butter or margarine.
4. Bake for 5 minutes.
5. Prepare sauce by combining shallots, red wine (or vinegar) and lemon juice in a small saucepan; bring to a boil and simmer over medium heat for 5 minutes.
6. Stir in dissolved cornstarch to thicken sauce; pour over fish.
7. Return to 400°F oven for 10 minutes.
8. Add the grapes during the last 5 minutes of baking and serve hot.

PIQUANT SCALLOPS

Yield: 4 servings

Exchange 1 serving for: 3 Meat Exchanges
and 2 Fat Exchanges
and ½ Bread Exchange

Ingredients: 1 lb. scallops
3 tbsps. fine dry bread crumbs
8 tsps. melted butter or margarine
1 tsp. Worcestershire sauce
2 tsps. lemon juice

Method:
1. Roll scallops in the bread crumbs. Arrange in 4 scallop shells, or in a shallow greased baking dish.
2. Pour mixture of melted butter or margarine, Worcestershire sauce and lemon juice over the scallops.
3. Bake in hot oven (450°F to 500°F) for 10 minutes.

CRAB FONDUE

Yield: 4 servings

Exchange 1 serving for: 3 Meat Exchanges
and 1 Bread Exchange
and ½ Milk Exchange

Ingredients: 1 tsp. butter or margarine
4 slices white bread
1 cup crab meat, flaked
5 slices (5 oz.) processed cheese, diced or grated
3 eggs, well beaten
1 cup skim milk
½ tsp. onion, chopped
1 tsp. salt
paprika to garnish

Method:
1. Preheat oven to 350°F.
2. Grease 1½ quart casserole with butter or margarine.
3. Alternate layers of torn bread, crab meat and cheese in casserole.
4. Combine beaten eggs, milk, onion and salt; pour evenly over mixture in casserole.
5. Sprinkle with paprika.
6. Bake at 350°F for 30 minutes.

SHRIMP FRIED RICE

Yield: 4 servings

Exchange 1 serving for: 1 Meat Exchange
and 2 Fat Exchanges
and 1½ Bread Exchanges
and 1 Vegetable Exchange List 2A

Ingredients: 1 cup onions, chopped
4 stalks celery, chopped
8 tsps. salad oil
2 cups cooked rice
One 4¼ oz. tin cocktail shrimps
½ cup canned water chestnuts, drained
¼ cup soy sauce

Method:
1. Sauté onions and celery in salad oil until pale yellow.
2. Add rice, shrimps, water chestnuts and soy sauce.
3. Stir until thoroughly mixed.
4. Cover and simmer for 10 minutes or until very hot; serve immediately.

MARINATED PORK CHOPS

Yield: 6 servings

Exchange 1 serving for: 3 Meat Exchanges
and 1 Calorie Poor Food List B

Ingredients: 6 loin pork chops, ¾ inch thick
1 clove garlic, finely chopped
1 tsp. caraway seeds
2 tsps. paprika
salt and freshly ground black pepper to taste
1 cup dry white wine

Method:
1. Arrange chops in shallow casserole so they do not touch.
2. Mix garlic, caraway seeds, paprika, salt and pepper, and sprinkle over chops.
3. Add wine; cover, and let chops marinate in the refrigerator (2 to 3 hours).
4. Preheat oven to 300°F.
5. Bake chops in marinade, uncovered, until tender (about 1½ hours).

VEAL A LA PROVENCALE

Yield: 6 servings

Exchange 1 serving for: 3 Meat Exchanges
and 1 Vegetable Exchange List 2A
and 2 Fat Exchanges

Ingredients: 1½ lbs. veal cutlet, cut into 6 thin even slices
2½ tbsps. flour for dredging
¼ cup olive oil
½ lb. fresh mushrooms, sliced
2 small cloves garlic, minced
½ cup dry white wine
4 medium raw tomatoes, peeled and chopped
salt and freshly ground black pepper to taste
parsley, chopped, to garnish

Method:
1. Pound veal slices lightly until very thin; dredge with flour.
2. Heat oil in a skillet; add veal and brown both sides.
3. Push veal to the side of the pan; add mushrooms and cook, stirring often (2 or 3 minutes).
4. Arrange mushrooms on veal; combine garlic, wine, tomatoes, salt and pepper, and spoon *around* meat.
5. Simmer about 10 minutes.
6. Serve sprinkled with parsley.

Note: ½ cup meat stock may be used in place of wine. See page 9.

BOEUF BOURGUIGNON

Yield: 4 servings
Exchange 1 serving for: 3 Meat Exchanges
and 1½ Fat Exchanges
and 1 Vegetable Exchange List 2B
and 1 Calorie Poor Food List B

Ingredients: 1 tbsp. butter or margarine
10 small onions, peeled
3 slices lean bacon, diced
1½ lbs. beef chuck, cut in 2 inch pieces
1 tbsp. flour
1 cup red wine
¼ cup beef stock. See page 8.
½ tsp. tomato paste
1 medium carrot, cut in pieces
1 garlic clove, crushed
salt and pepper to taste
¼ lb. small fresh mushrooms
5 tsps. butter or margarine

Method: 1. Heat 1 tbsp. butter or margarine in heavy casserole; add onion and brown; then add bacon and brown.
2. Remove both onion and bacon and reserve.
3. Add meat and brown; stir in flour and cook 1 minute.
4. Add red wine, stock, tomato paste, carrot, garlic and season with salt and pepper; simmer 1½ hours.
5. Add onions and bacon and cook ¾ hour.
6. Add mushrooms which have been lightly sautéed in 5 tsps. butter or margarine; cook 15 minutes.
7. Serve, dusted with chopped parsley.

Note: 1 cup beef stock may be substituted for 1 cup red wine.

PEPPER STEAK

Yield: 4 servings
Exchange 1 serving for: 3 Meat Exchanges
and 2 Fat Exchanges
and 1 Calorie Poor Food List B

Ingredients: 1 lb. sirloin steak, cut ½ inch thick
1½ tbsps. cracked black pepper
½ tsp. salt
1½ tbsps. butter or margarine
1 tbsp. olive or salad oil
3 tbsps. chicken or veal stock. See page 8.
2 tbsps. white wine or brandy

Method: 1. Rub both sides of steak with black pepper, working it in with the ball of the hand.
2. Sprinkle both sides of steak lightly with salt.
3. Heat butter or margarine and oil in 12 inch skillet.
4. Add steak and sear on each side; then cook 5 to 7 minutes on each side.
5. Transfer steak to a serving platter.
6. From skillet, drain drippings, leaving 1 tbsp.
7. Add stock and wine to skillet and blend.
8. Heat and pour over steak; serve at once.

Note: Wine or brandy may be replaced by adding 2 more tbsps. chicken or veal stock.

COQ AU VIN

Yield: 4 servings

Exchange 1 serving for: 3 Meat Exchanges
and 2 Fat Exchanges
and 1 Vegetable Exchange List 2A

Ingredients: 1½ tbsps. butter or margarine
2 slices bacon, diced
2 lb. broiler chicken, split equally into 4
10 small silverskin onions, peeled
½ clove garlic, minced
3 medium mushrooms, sliced
2 tbsps. brandy
⅓ bay leaf
dash each: thyme, salt and freshly ground pepper
1 cup dry red wine
2 tsps. flour
2 tsps. butter or margarine
1 cup beef stock
1 tbsp. fresh parsley, chopped
¼ tsp. fresh tarragon, minced

Method: 1. Heat butter and bacon in heavy casserole; add chicken and brown.
2. Add onions, garlic and mushrooms.
3. Add brandy and ignite; when flame burns out, add bay leaf, thyme, salt and pepper and wine; bring to a boil; cover and simmer for 15 minutes.
4. Make paste with flour and butter; add to casserole and stir until thickened; add beef stock.
5. Cover; simmer 1 hour; garnish with parsley and tarragon.

APPLE CIDER SALAD

Yield: 4 servings

Exchange 1 serving for: 1 Fruit Exchange

Ingredients: 2¼ tsps. unflavoured gelatin
3 tbsps. cold water
1 tsp. artificial liquid sweetener
1 cup apple cider or apple juice
1 tbsp. lemon juice
¼ tsp. salt
½ medium apple, finely chopped

Method:
1. Soften gelatin in cold water.
2. Combine artificial liquid sweetener, cider, lemon juice and salt.
3. Heat and add to softened gelatin, stirring until gelatin is dissolved.
4. Cool until mixture begins to thicken.
5. Fold in apples.
6. Pour into 2-cup mould or divide into 4 individual moulds.
7. Chill until firm.
8. Unmould on crisp greens.

HOSTESS SALAD

Yield: 4 servings, each containing 2 egg halves

Exchange 1 serving for: 1 Meat Exchange
and 1 Vegetable Exchange List 2B

Ingredients: 1 tbsp. artificially sweetened lime jelly powder
⅛ tsp. salt
1 cup boiling water
1 cup cold water
2 tsps. vinegar
dash of cayenne pepper
4 hard boiled eggs, peeled
1 tsp. prepared mustard
1 tbsp. whole milk
dash each salt and pepper
1 cup celery, chopped
2 tbsps. pimento, chopped
2 tbsps. onion, minced

Method:
1. Dissolve jelly powder and ⅛ tsp. salt in boiling water.
2. Add cold water, 1 tsp. vinegar and cayenne; chill until partially thickened.
3. Meanwhile, halve eggs lengthwise and remove yolks.
4. Sieve yolks; blend in prepared mustard, 1 tsp. vinegar, milk, salt and pepper to taste.
5. Fill whites with yolk mixture.
6. Spoon just enough thickened gelatin into a 1 quart ring mould to form a layer about ¼ inch thick.
7. Arrange eggs, cut side down on gelatin in mould.
8. Add celery, pimento and onion to remaining gelatin.
9. Spoon this mixture over eggs, spreading it evenly in mould.
10. Chill until firm.
11. Divide servings so each contains two egg halves.

ENGLISH APPLE TRIFLE

Yield: 8 servings

Exchange 1 serving for: 1 Fruit Exchange
and 1 Bread Exchange

Ingredients: 4 medium cooking apples, sliced
1 tbsp. water
2¼ tsps. artificial liquid sweetener
dash salt
¼ tsp. ground nutmeg
½ tsp. grated lemon peel
12 lady fingers
½ recipe Soft Custard. See page 100.

Method:
1. Place apples and water in saucepan; cover and cook over low heat until tender.
2. Remove from heat and put through a sieve.
3. Add liquid sweetener, salt, nutmeg and lemon peel; mix well and cool.
4. Arrange lady fingers, applesauce and cold custard in layers in 8″ square pan, with lady fingers on the bottom and custard on top.
5. Chill until ready to serve.
6. Serve with skim milk topping if desired. See page 129.

EGGNOG CHIFFON PIE

Yield: 12 servings

Exchange 1 serving for: 1 Bread Exchange
and 1 Fat Exchange
and ½ Fruit Exchange
and ½ Milk Exchange

Ingredients: I tbsp. unflavoured gelatin
¼ cup cold water
1½ cups skim milk
1½ tbsps. artificial liquid sweetener
¼ tsp. salt
3 tbsps. cornstarch
3 eggs, separated
1 tsp. vanilla
1 tbsp. rum flavouring
one 8 inch baked pie shell. See page 41 (Tourtiere).

Method: 1. Soften gelatin in cold water.

2. Combine ¾ cup of milk, liquid sweetener and salt in top of double boiler.

3. When hot, stir in paste made from cornstarch and remaining ¾ cup milk.

4. Cook over boiling water, stirring constantly until thickened.

5. Add a little of the hot mixture to beaten egg yolk; then carefully stir egg yolk mixture into remaining hot liquid and cook 2 minutes.

6. Remove from heat; stir in softened gelatin until dissolved.

7. Chill until mixture begins to set.

8. Stir in vanilla and rum flavouring.

9. Fold in stiffly beaten egg whites.

10. Spoon into baked pie shell; chill until firm.

11. Garnish, if desired, with skim milk topping. See page 129.

PEACHES FLAMBE

Yield: 4 servings

Exchange 1 serving for: 1 Fruit Exchange

Ingredients: 4 fresh peaches, sliced, or 8 unsweetened canned peach halves

¼ cup unsweetened orange juice

½ tsp. artificial liquid sweetener

3 tbsps. brandy

Method: 1. Combine peaches, orange juice and artificial liquid sweetener and bring to a boil.

2. Transfer to 4 serving dishes.

3. Warm brandy, pour evenly over each portion; ignite.

4. Serve immediately.

Note: You may serve "flaming" over ice cream; 1/6 pint of ice cream per serving, and increase exchange value by **adding** 1 Fruit Exchange and 1 Fat Exchange.

GLAZED STRAWBERRY TARTS

Yield: 6 servings

Exchange 1 serving for: ½ Fruit Exchange
and 1 Calorie Poor Food List B
and ½ Bread Exchange
and 1 Fat Exchange

Ingredients: 6 small tart shells. See page 103.
1½ tsps. unflavoured gelatin
2 tbsps. cold water
3 cups small fresh strawberries
1½ tbsps. artificial liquid sweetener
red food colouring
1 tbsp. lemon juice

Method:
1. Soften gelatin in cold water.
2. Wash and stem berries; add liquid sweetener.
3. Press 1 cup of the berries through a strainer.
4. Add food colouring, if desired.
5. Add lemon juice and bring to a boil.
6. Remove from heat; add softened gelatin, stirring to dissolve.
7. Chill until mixture begins to thicken.
8. Arrange remaining 2 cups whole berries in tart shells, dividing them evenly; cover with glaze.

PARTY TREATS

For gala days when special treats mean so much.

FUDGE

Yield: 8 servings

Exchange 1 serving for: ½ Fat Exchange (when rolled in pudding powder)
or 1 Fat Exchange (when rolled in nuts)

Ingredients: 1 square semi-sweetened chocolate
¼ cup evaporated milk
1 tsp. vanilla
½ tsp. artificial liquid sweetener
1 package vanilla or chocolate artificially sweetened pudding powder **or** 8 tsps. finely chopped nuts

Method: 1. Melt chocolate in top of double boiler over boiling water.
2. Add evaporated milk and mix well.
3. Cook for 2 or 3 minutes. Add vanilla and artificial liquid sweetener.
4. Spread on small foil pie tin or saucer; chill.
5. Divide into 8 equal portions; form each into a small ball and roll lightly in pudding powder; **or** roll each ball in 1 tsp. chopped nuts.

JELLY DELIGHTS

Yield: 64 one inch squares or 32 servings

Exchange 2 one inch squares for: 1 Calorie Free Food List A

Ingredients: 1 tbsp. bulk or 2 envelopes artificially sweetened jelly powder (any flavour)
2 tbsps. skim milk powder **or** artificially sweetened pudding powder
1⅓ cups water

Method: 1. Proceed as directed in instructions on label of jelly powder.
2. Pour into shallow 8″ cake tin (will be about ½″ in depth).
3. Chill until set.
4. Cut into 64 one inch squares (or equal number of fancy shapes) and roll each in skim milk powder or pudding powder; keep chilled until served.

Variations: 1. Add small amount finely chopped orange rind to orange jelly.
2. Add drop or two of concentrated or canned lemon juice to lime or lemon jelly.

WALNUT SPECIALS

Yield: 8 servings

Exchange 1 serving for: 1 Fat Exchange
and 1 Calorie Poor Food List B

Ingredients: 2½ oz. (5 tbsps.) white cream cheese
1 tbsp. artificially sweetened jam spread
4 social tea cookies, crushed
6 walnuts, chopped fine

Method: 1. Soften cream cheese at room temperature for ½ hour.
2. Add artificially sweetened jam spread and crushed cookies.
3. Beat with electric mixer or rotary beater.
4. Spread on square cake tin or other suitable container.
5. Chill for about ½ hour.
6. Remove from refrigerator and cut into 8 squares; form into balls and roll in walnuts.

146

"FROSTICLE"

Exchange 1 "frosticle" for: 1 Calorie Free Food List A

Ingredients: 1 tbsp. **or** 2 envelopes of flavoured artificially sweetened
jelly powder

1 cup boiling water

2 cups cold water or artificially sweetened ginger ale

Method: 1. Dissolve jelly powder in boiling water.

2. Add cold water or ginger ale.

3. Freeze in ice-cube tray or containers available in retail
stores for this purpose.

4. Wooden sticks may be inserted when partially frozen.

NUTS AND BOLTS

Yield: 6 cups

Exchange ⅜ cup (containing 5 peanuts) for: ½ Bread Exchange
and ½ Fat Exchange

Ingredients: 6 cups mixed prepared (unsweetened) cereal e.g. Cheer-
ios, Rice Chex, Corn Chex, Shreddies, and small pret-
zel sticks

5 tbsps. plus 1 tsp. butter or margarine

6 to 8 oz. peanuts, shelled

2 tsps. Worcestershire sauce

2 tsps. Tabasco sauce

2 tsps. savoury salt

2 tsps. garlic salt (optional)

Method: 1. Preheat oven to 225°F.

2. Use any combination of cereals; be sure to select a variety
of shapes; combine in large shallow baking pan.

3. Melt butter or margarine and add seasonings.

4. Pour gradually over cereal mixture, stirring to mix thoroughly.

5. Bake in **slow** oven for 1½ hours, stirring often.

6. Cool; store in closed container.

PEANUT CRUNCH

Yield: 6 servings

Exchange 1 serving for: 1 Fat Exchange
and 1 Calorie Poor Food List B

Ingredients: 2½ tbsps. peanut butter

2 tsps. artificially sweetened jam spread

4 graham wafers or social teas, crushed

10 peanuts (**or** 6 walnuts) chopped fine

Method: 1. Mix peanut butter, jam spread, and crushed biscuits.

2. Form into six balls.

3. Roll in chopped nuts.

147

BEVERAGES

Tea and coffee, when served clear, are listed as Calorie Free Foods List A in the Meal Planning booklet. Variations of these, and other suggestions for beverages are included here to give some ideas for adding variety to meals. In many cases, variety is achieved with a minimum number of exchanges. Tempting fluids are also a help in times of illness, as they provide easily assimilated nourishment.

Recipes and suggestions for soft and liquid diets are included in a separate section. See pages 153-159.

HOT BEVERAGES

Coffee

Whether instant or ground coffee is used, is a matter of personal preference.

Instant coffee made in bulk, and served piping hot from a coffee pot or carafe, has good flavour.

If coffee is to be brewed, choose the grind which suits your coffee maker. Buy coffee in small quantities to ensure freshness and store it in an air-tight container. Use a sparkling-clean coffee maker. Measure coffee and water exactly, and follow carefully the instructions for the type of coffee maker used. Brew just long enough to extract best flavour, and serve steaming hot.

Café Au Lait

Heat milk allowance just to scalding point in double boiler or over low heat. Combine with an equal amount of strong, hot coffee by pouring both into the cup at the same time. If desired, add artificial liquid sweetener to taste.

148

Spiced Coffee

Brew coffee as usual, adding a mixture of spices to the grounds. A pleasant combination of spices for 4 cups of coffee is: 4 whole cloves; ⅛ tsp. nutmeg; ⅛ tsp. cinnamon. Serve the coffee with cinnamon sticks as stirrers.

Tea

Bring fresh cold water to a rapid boil. Allow 1 tea bag or 1 heaping tsp. tea leaves for each 2 teacups of water.

Heat the teapot (not metal) by pouring in a little boiling water. Empty the pot, immediately put in the measured tea, and add the freshly boiled water.

Let steep for 3 to 5 minutes. Stir, and serve at once.

For variety, experiment with green tea, oolong, or special blends.

Hot Spiced Tea: Stud lemon slices with whole cloves. Place 1 lemon slice in each tea cup, add 1-inch stick of cinnamon, and pour in the hot tea.

COCOA

Yield: 1 serving
Exchange for: 1 Milk Exchange
　　　　　　　　and 2 Calorie Poor Foods List B
Ingredients: ½ cup whole milk
　　　　　　　2 tsps. powdered cocoa (not instant)
　　　　　　　artificial liquid sweetener
Method: 1. Measure milk into a saucepan, and cocoa into a cup. Remove 1 tbsp. of the milk, and blend with the cocoa powder.
　　　　　2. Scald remaining milk, adding artificial liquid sweetener. Gradually stir scalded milk into cocoa mixture.
　　　　　3. Sprinkle with grated nutmeg if desired.
Note: If Fat Allowance permits, top with 1 rounded tbsp. whipped cream (add 1 Fat Exchange).

HOT SPICED APPLE JUICE

Yield: 4 servings (⅔ cup each)
Exchange 1 serving for: 2 Fruit Exchanges
Ingredients: 2⅔ cups unsweetened apple juice
　　　　　　　½ tsp. whole allspice
　　　　　　　6 whole cloves
　　　　　　　1 two-inch stick cinnamon
Method: 1. Add spices to apple juice in saucepan; bring just to a boil.
　　　　　2. Strain into heated glasses or mugs and serve.

SPICY GRAPE TODDY

Yield: four 4-oz. servings
Exchange 1 serving for: 1 Fruit Exchange
Ingredients: 10 oz. unsweetened grape juice
6 oz. unsweetened orange juice
¼ cup lemon juice
½ tsp. artificial liquid sweetener
1 whole cinnamon stick
Method: 1. Mix the three juices.
2. Add cinnamon stick and simmer 15 to 20 minutes.
3. Add artificial liquid sweetener just before serving; remove cinnamon stick; serve hot.

COLD BEVERAGES

Iced Coffee

Pour double-strength coffee over ice cubes or cracked ice in tall glasses. If ice supply is limited, allow coffee to cool first to room temperature (in which case, coffee may be made a little less strong). If desired, add artificial liquid sweetener to taste.
Note: If Fat Allowance permits, top with 1 rounded tbsp. whipped cream (add 1 Fat Exchange).

Iced Tea

Brew tea double-strength. Fill tall glasses with ice, and carefully pour in the tea. Some blends of tea are less likely than others to turn cloudy when poured over ice — e.g. certain blends of English Breakfast Tea.

Green and oolong teas are pleasant, but pale in colour, and are best suited for use with fruit juices in making punch.

Serve iced tea with a wedge of lemon and a sprig of mint, and with artificial liquid sweetener if desired.

TEA PUNCH

Yield: six 6-oz. servings
Exchange 1 serving for: 1 Fruit Exchange
Ingredients: 1 cup tea (made from 2 tsps. green or oolong tea and 1 cup water)
½ cup lemon juice
½ cup unsweetened pineapple juice
1½ cups unsweetened orange juice
1 cup water
artificial liquid sweetener to taste
Method: Combine all ingredients; chill, and serve over ice.

QUICK PUNCH

Mix 1 Fruit Exchange, as juice, with artificially sweetened ginger ale or with soda water.

Serving Hints: When using a punch bowl, chill punch with larger pieces of ice, made by freezing water in cans from frozen juices.

To carry out the colour scheme of a party, first tint the water for the ice with pure food colouring. Freeze mint leaves, tiny wedges of orange and lemon slices, or fresh berries or cherries in the ice.

CRANBERRY PUNCH

Yield: ten 4-oz. servings
Exchange 1 serving for: ½ Fruit Exchange
Ingredients: 1 cup raw cranberries
1½ cups water
¾ cup lemon juice
1¼ cups unsweetened orange juice
artificial liquid sweetener
2 cups soda water
Method: 1. Sort and wash cranberries. Put into saucepan and add water; cover and cook until skins pop.
2. Press cranberries through a sieve; add fruit juices and sweeten to taste with artificial liquid sweetener; chill.
3. At serving time, pour over ice and add the soda water.

HOLIDAY SUNSHINE PUNCH

Yield: five 7-oz. servings
Exchange 1 serving for: 1 Fruit Exchange
Ingredients: 2 cups unsweetened pineapple juice
1 tbsp. lemon juice
2 cans (10 oz. each) low calorie ginger ale
OR low calorie lemon-lime beverage
Method: 1. Chill soda pop and juice.
2. Mix and serve immediately over cracked ice.

MILK SHAKE

Yield: four 6-oz. servings
Exchange 1 serving for: 1 Milk Exchange
and 1 Fruit Exchange
and 1 Fat Exchange
Ingredients: ⅔ brick ice cream (chocolate, strawberry or vanilla)
2 cups whole milk
Method: 1. Blend.
2. Serve ice cold.

BANANA PUNCH

Yield: four 5-oz. servings

Exchange 1 serving for: 1 Milk Exchange
and ½ Fruit Exchange

Ingredients: 2 cups whole milk
1 medium banana
nutmeg

Method: 1. Mash banana.
2. Pour milk over banana and beat well.
3. Chill and pour into glasses; sprinkle with nutmeg.

FLOAT

Yield: four 10-oz. servings

Exchange 1 serving for: 1 Fruit Exchange
and 1 Fat Exchange

Ingredients: 4 - 10 oz. bottles or cans low calorie beverage
⅔ brick vanilla ice cream

Method: 1. Divide ice cream into 4 servings and put one into each of 4 tall glasses.
2. Add 1 bottle or can of low calorie beverage to each.
3. Stir to blend.

LIQUID and SOFT DIETS

The diabetic patient who is in the hospital faces no problem when the doctor orders a liquid or soft diet. However, when the diabetic is ill at home, adapting daily meal plans to liquid or soft foods, often causes bewilderment and consternation. The following suggestions will be of help when such a situation arises.

But first a word of caution! When a diabetic first becomes ill, either the diabetic or some member of the family should get in touch with the doctor immediately. No changes should be made in the medical routine (insulin or tablets) or the dietary pattern without the doctor's permission. His instructions should be carefully followed.

These instructions might mean that the three meals be broken down into six or more feedings.

Included on the following pages are foods from the different exchange lists which are readily adaptable to liquid and soft diets. In addition there are a number of recipes.

Milk Exchange List 1:

Milk is allowed in the diabetic diet in a stated amount. However, the milk allowance may be used in a variety of ways.

Milk may be served plain, either cold or hot as a beverage, **or** it may be served in combination with other foods such as egg-nogs, soups, gruel, etc. Recipes including milk will be found in the last section of this chapter.

153

For one Vegetable Exchange List 2A, use one of the following:

⅔ cup tomato juice
or ⅔ cup mixed vegetable juice
or one of the following soups: 1. Chicken Rice Soup
                                2. Canned Condensed Soups

See recipes which follow in this chapter (page 156) and soup recipes commencing on page 8.

For one Fruit Exchange List 3, use one of the following (unsweetened):

⅓ cup apple juice
or ½ cup orange juice
or ½ cup grapefruit juice
or ¼ cup grape juice
or ⅓ cup pineapple juice
or ¼ cup prune juice
or 1/6 pint brick plain vanilla, chocolate, or strawberry ice cream.
  (Take off 1 Fat Exchange.)

Note: Dietetic or artificially sweetened ginger ale is a Calorie Free Food List A and may be mixed with any of the above juices without changing the food value. Grape juice and ginger ale are particularly good mixed together.

For one Bread Exchange List 4, use one of the following:

cooked cereal — ½ cup
or prepared cereal — ¾ cup flaked
                     1 cup puffed
or 3 arrowroot biscuits
or 4 social tea biscuits
or 4 graham wafers
or 1 slice enriched white bread, plain or toasted
or use 1½ Fruit Exchanges from List 3 in place of 1 Bread Exchange.

For instance, if using orange juice for the Bread Exchange, the amount should be worked out as follows:

½ cup orange juice is 1 Fruit Exchange, therefore, ¾ cup orange juice would be 1½ Fruit Exchanges or the equivalent in food value of 1 Bread Exchange.

154

Meat Exchange List 5

In the acute stage of illness, foods from the Meat Exchange List may pose a problem. In such a case the doctor should be consulted about the best routine to follow under the circumstances. His instructions should be carefully followed.

Eggs may be used in eggnogs or custards.

One 3½ ounce tin of puréed 'baby' meat may be exchanged for: 3 Meat Exchanges.

Fat Exchange List 6

Frequently in the acute stage of illness, fat is not well tolerated. This is often the case if the person is nauseated. Again, the doctor will advise the best procedure to follow.

Cream may be added to beverages such as tea, coffee, or cocoa. It may be used in the preparation of soft desserts or served with the desserts.

Calorie Free Food List A

When fever is present, the doctor may wish the patient to increase the fluid intake — and this is when the "free" foods come into their own.

Some of these are:

1. Clear Broth: chicken, beef, etc., from which all the fat has been removed.

2. Consommé

3. Bouillon (canned or cubes)

4. Meat extract concentrates (diluted with water)

5. Artificially sweetened carbonated beverages available in liquid or tablet form, and in a variety of flavours.

6. Water

7. Clear Tea or Coffee

For one Calorie Poor Food List B, use one of the following:

⅓ cup Tomato Juice
or ⅓ cup Mixed Vegetable Juice

CHICKEN RICE SOUP (Home-made)

Yield: 1 serving

Exchange for: 1 Calorie Free Food List A
and 1 Vegetable Exchange List 2A

Ingredients: ⅔ cup clear fat-free chicken broth, seasoned to taste
3 level tbsps. cooked rice

Method: Heat broth and rice together to desired serving temperature.

Variations with the same exchange value:

Chicken Noodle — use 3 tbsps. cooked noodles in place of the rice.

Beef Rice or Beef Noodle — make as above but use clear beef broth instead of chicken broth.

Beef with Barley — make as above and add 2 tbsps. cooked barley.

CANNED CONDENSED SOUPS

Yield: 1 serving

Exchange for: 1 Vegetable Exchange List 2A
and 1 Milk Exchange (if milk is used for liquid)

Ingredients: 3 level tbsps. canned condensed soup, undiluted
⅔ cup water, consommé, or clear fat-free broth
or ½ cup whole milk

Method: Mix above ingredients together and heat.

GRUEL

Yield: 1 serving

Exchange for: ½ Bread Exchange
and 1 Milk Exchange

Ingredients: ¼ cup cooked cereal
½ cup whole milk heated
artificial liquid sweetener to taste if desired
f.g. ground nutmeg or ground cinnamon

Method:
1. Add hot milk to the hot cereal.
2. Mix well so that there are no lumps.
3. Add artificial liquid sweetener.
4. Reheat; sprinkle with cinnamon or nutmeg if desired.
5. Serve hot.

BREAD AND MILK

Yield: 1 serving
Exchange for: 1 Bread Exchange
and 1 Milk Exchange
and 1 Fat Exchange
Ingredients: 1 slice bread
1 tsp. butter or margarine
½ cup whole milk
Method: 1. Butter bread with 1 tsp. butter or margarine.
2. Cut into cubes and place in cereal bowl.
3. Heat milk and pour over the bread cubes; serve hot.

OMELET

Yield: 1 serving
Exchange for: 2 Meat Exchanges
and 1 Fat Exchange
Ingredients: 2 eggs, separated
pinch of baking powder (omit for low sodium diets)
1 tbsp. water
salt and pepper to taste
1 tsp. butter or margarine
Method: 1. Beat egg whites until stiff; add baking powder.
2. Beat egg yolks until light; add seasonings and water, and beat slightly.
3. Heat an omelet pan and add butter or margarine; have sides and bottom of pan well greased.
4. Cut and fold egg whites into the egg yolk mixture.
5. Have pan very hot; pour in the egg mixture; spread evenly; reduce heat.
6. Cook slowly until omelet is set; place in moderate oven (350°F) to dry slightly on top.
7. Remove from oven, fold, and turn out; garnish and serve at once.

FRUIT NOG

Yield: 1 serving
Exchange for: 1 Meat Exchange
and 1 Fruit Exchange
Ingredients: 1 egg
½ cup orange juice or other fruit juice to the equivalent of 1 Fruit Exchange
Method: 1. Beat egg.
2. Add fruit juice and mix well; serve ice cold.

EGG NOG

Yield: 1 serving

Exchange for: 1 Meat Exchange
and 1 Milk Exchange

Ingredients: 1 egg
½ cup whole milk
artificial liquid sweetener to taste
1 or 2 drops vanilla

Method: 1. Beat egg and artificial liquid sweetener together.
2. Add milk and beat together until mixed, but not frothy.
3. Add vanilla; serve ice cold.

LEMONADE

Yield: 1 serving

Exchange for: 1 Calorie Poor Food List B

Ingredients: 1 tbsp. lemon juice or 1 tbsp. unsweetened canned or
frozen lemon juice
½ tsp. or less artificial liquid sweetener
water
ice cubes

Method: Mix above ingredients together, adding ice cubes last.

HOT LEMONADE

Make as cold lemonade, omitting the ice cubes and adding hot water
instead of cold. Exchange as for cold lemonade.

GRAPE JUICE AND GINGER ALE

Yield: 1 serving

Exchange for: 1 Fruit Exchange
and 1 Calorie Free Food List A

Ingredients: ¼ cup unsweetened grape juice
artificially sweetened ginger ale
ice cubes if desired

Method: 1. Place grape juice in a glass.
2. Fill glass with ginger ale and mix.
3. Add ice if desired and serve.

Variations: Other fruit juices may also be mixed with artificially
sweetened ginger ale without adding to their food value.

LIMEADE

Yield: 1 serving

Exchange for: 1 Calorie Poor Food List B

Ingredients: 1 tbsp, unsweetened lime juice, fresh, canned or frozen
½ tsp. or less artificial liquid sweetener
water
ice cubes

Method: Mix above ingredients together, adding the ice cubes last.

ORANGE AND PINEAPPLE DRINK

Yield: 1 serving

Exchange for: 2 Fruit Exchanges

Ingredients: ½ cup orange juice
⅓ cup pineapple juice
ice cubes if desired

Method: 1. Mix fruit juices together.

2. Add ice cubes or chopped ice; serve.

OTHER SUGGESTIONS FOR LIQUID AND SOFT DIETS

1. Artificially sweetened applesauce, ½ cup equals 1 Fruit Exchange.

2. Baked Custard — see page 99.

3. Fruit Whips and Fluffs — See pages 97 and 100.

4. Flavoured artificially sweetened jellies — Calorie Free Food List A.

5. Ice Cream — 1/6 pint brick ice cream or one ice cream roll may be
exchanged for 1 Fat Exchange
and 1 Fruit Exchange

6. Ice Cream Jelly Bavarian — see page 107.

7. Rice or Tapioca Pudding — see pages 107 and 108.

8. Soft Custard and other soft desserts — see dessert section commencing page 96.

9. Coddled, scrambled or poached egg.

CANNING, FREEZING AND PICKLING

For those who have the facilities, home preservation of fruits and vegetables at the peak of their season is an economical way of adding variety to the menu.

Bulletins prepared by the Food Advisory Services, Canada Department of Agriculture, cover thoroughly the general directions for canning and freezing and have sections on the preservation of food without sugar. Single copies of the booklets, "Home Canning of Fruits and Vegetables" and "Freezing Foods", may be obtained free of charge by writing to:

Information Division,
Canada Department of Agriculture,
Ottawa, Ontario   K1A 0C7.

Those persons on restricted sodium diets are reminded that the step in the prevention of discolouration called a "brine bath" used for certain fruits, must be avoided. But satisfactory results can be obtained by putting the fruit into acidulated water instead of brine bath. The acid to use could be vinegar or lemon juice — just sufficient to retain colour of the fruit.

CANNING

The water pack method of canning fruit is one which has been used successfully for years. No sweetener is added during the processing. A great many people prefer the fruit canned this way and without the addition of artificial sweeteners. If, however, you prefer the fruit sweetened, follow the directions as given. About an hour or two before serving, open the fruit and place in an open container. Add artificial sweetener to taste and mix well; the sweetener will permeate the fruit as well as the liquid. Some people like to heat the fruit and sweetener together, as they feel this gives a more evenly distributed sweetness.

WATER PACKED FRUIT

General Method:

1. Have all equipment ready.
2. Check and sterilize jars.
3. Boil small equipment you will use in the actual filling of the jars.
4. Use only firm fresh fruit. Wash carefully. Blanch.

   To Blanch Fruit:

   Tie fruit in square of cheesecloth or thin muslin, or place in colander. Plunge the fruit and colander or cloth into boiling water for 50 to 60 seconds. There should be three to four times as much water as fruit.

   Reasons for Blanching:

   To make removal of skins easier (tomatoes or peaches).

   To shrink fruit so more can be packed into the jars.

   To set colour.
5. Cold Dip. Take quickly from hot water and plunge into cold water. Plunge it once or twice, but do not let it sit in the water any longer than necessary.
6. Slip off the skins or peel and pack fruit immediately into hot jars which have been sterilized. Do not let the jars cool.
7. Pour boiling water over the fruit in the jars, filling up to ½″ from the top. Be sure there is no fruit above the level of the water.
8. Run a sterilized knife around in the jars to let out the air bubbles.
9. Put on the rubber rings which have been dipped into boiling water.
10. If using vacuum-type jars, seal the jars tightly at this point.
11. If using glass top jars, screw metal band tightly. Then loosen slightly, unscrewing not more than 1 inch.
12. Place filled sealers 1″ apart on rack in the boiling water bath. Have the water 2″ above the tops of the jars. Do not pour boiling water directly on sealers as jars might crack.
13. Place cover on bath, and bring to boiling point.
14. Start to count processing time from moment water is actually **boiling vigorously,** not just beginning to show bubbles. Keep water boiling until processing is finished, adding water if necessary to keep level 2″ above jars.
15. See table below for the processing times for the various fruits.
16. When processing time is up, immediately remove sealers from water to prevent overcooking. Place on folded dry cloth or newspapers.

    To avoid cracking, do not place hot sealers in draughts or on metal or porcelain surfaces.

17. As soon as all bubbling in sealers has ceased, tighten tops on screwtop glass top sealers by giving the metal bands a final turn. Vacuum-type sealers require no further tightening since the seal is formed as they cool.

18. Cool sealers in an upright position, out of draughts. Leave space between sealers when cooling.

Test for Seal: see page 163.

FRUIT PROCESSING TABLE

Soft Fruits	Preparation	Boiling Water	Time of Processing
Berries Blackberries Blueberries	Wash, hull and pack in jars.	Fill jars with boiling water to ½" of top	16 mins.
Dewberries Raspberries Strawberries Cherries Apricots Peaches Plums	Blanch by dipping in boiling water once or twice.	as above	16 mins.
Rhubarb	Cut in ½" lengths and blanch as above.	as above	16 mins.
Hard Fruits			
Apples Pears Quinces	Peel, core cut in halves or slices; Blanch twice for ½ minute each	as above	20 mins.
Pineapple	Cold dip. Do not blanch.	as above	30 mins.

Use preserving kettle with a false bottom or wire rack to keep jars from touching bottom of vessel and so permit free circulation of water.

Test for Seal:

Screw top jars: When cold, carefully invert each one for a minute or two, to see if there is leakage.

Vacuum-type sealers with metal lids: When cold, gently tap lids with a spoon. If properly sealed, they will give a clear ringing note, and be curved slightly inwards. It is not necessary to invert vacuum-type sealers to test for seal.

FREEZING

Freezing is a very satisfactory method of preserving food. It is a convenient way to retain good colour, flavour and food value. Persons on diets will find this method of keeping food very helpful as dishes may be prepared ahead of time, labelled with the exchange value, brought out, cooked and served in a minimum of time. Most family-tested recipes can be used. For example: a casserole or recipe for 6 can be prepared, divided into 6 portions, placed in moisture proof containers, labelled with the contents and stored in the freezer until required. Such planning makes for economy with variety.

Persons living alone who have access to freezer space can buy more easily and overcome the common problem of shopping and cooking for one. Purchase enough for several meals. Have one meal now and freeze the rest for future use.

Points to Remember in Successful Freezing:
1. Use good quality food.
2. Prepare carefully according to freezer tables.
3. Use moisture proof wrapping; tie or seal securely, because food dries and loses its appearance and flavour if not sealed properly; label and date.
4. Freeze small quantities; freeze promptly after preparation, at 0°F to —10°F and store at this temperature until required.
5. Thaw foods with care; a good place is in the refrigerator; use thawed foods as soon as possible.
6. Do not overcook frozen vegetables.
7. Cook thawed meats as you would fresh meats; if meat must be cooked from the frozen state, it will take longer and use more fuel or electricity.

Freezing Fruits

When freezing fruits without sugar, for better flavour use fully ripened fruit. Part of the fruit may be crushed to make juice. The more juice there is to cover the fruit, the better the colour and flavour.

Fruits with a high acid content, such as strawberries, gooseberries, currants, cranberries and rhubarb, freeze very well without sugar. Fruits which discolour, such as peaches and apples, may be packed with ascorbic acid, which can be purchased specially for this purpose with the directions for use on the container.

The ascorbic acid crystals can be dissolved in water and sprinkled over the prepared fruit just before packing. Mix carefully and pack the fruit covered with its own juice or cover with water in which ascorbic acid has been dissolved.

Fresh strawberries are washed, hulled and packed in plastic bags or tight containers, with no special treatment. Raspberries can be spread out on a cookie sheet and put in the freezer until frozen hard and then packed in bags. They will hold their shape until brought out to be thawed. Serve while there are still a few ice crystals in the fruit. It will be firm and of good flavour.

Freezing Vegetables

Blanching is essential for the best results in freezing most vegetables. It destroys the enzymes which cause the vegetables to spoil or toughen. It prevents loss of flavour, colour and texture. It increases the time the vegetables can be stored in the freezer, without losing quality. Blanching also softens the vegetables enough to make them easier to pack in the freezer containers. To blanch the vegetables see directions under Canning (page 161). Blanching time will vary from 2 to 9 minutes. Consult a freezing time table as provided with the instructions which came with your freezer or see the table in "Freezing Foods" from the Canada Department of Agriculture.

Freezing Meat, Poultry and Fish

See "Care and Handling", page 35.

CAUTION: Do not refreeze meat which is thawed. It is better to cook it and then refreeze if necessary.

FREEZING HOME PREPARED FOODS: With a few exceptions prepared dishes such as stews, casseroles, bread, rolls and sandwiches can be frozen successfully.

YOUR FREEZER: A book of instruction is supplied with every freezer. It will have suggestions to help you get the most out of your freezer and how to take care of it.

SUGARLESS GRAPE JELLY

Yield: 2¾ cups

Exchange 1 tbsp. for: 1 Calorie Poor Food List B

Ingredients: 2 tbsps. gelatin
24 oz. unsweetened grape juice (cold)
2 tbsps. lemon juice
2 tbsps. artificial liquid sweetener

Method: 1. Measure grape juice into saucepan.
2. Add lemon juice; sprinkle gelatin over top of grape juice.
3. Gradually bring to a boil stirring to dissolve the gelatin; boil 1 minute.
4. Remove from heat and stir in sweetener.
5. Pour into small sterilized glass containers; cover and let cool.
6. Store in refrigerator.

SUGARLESS STRAWBERRY JAM

Yield: 2½ cups

Exchange 1 tbsp. for: 1 Calorie Poor Food List B

Ingredients: 5 cups cleaned firm strawberries
¼ tsp. red food colouring
2 oz. (1 pkg.) powdered fruit pectin
1 tbsp. lemon juice
3½ tsps. artificial liquid sweetener

Method: 1. Crush strawberries in 1½ quart saucepan; stir in food colouring.
2. Add fruit pectin and lemon juice.
3. Bring to a boil and boil 1 minute.
4. Remove from heat; add liquid sweetener and continue to stir for 2 minutes.
5. Pour into several small freezer containers; cover tightly and freeze.
6. Thaw before serving; refrigerate unused portion.

CHERRY OLIVES

Exchange 2 cherries for: 1 Calorie Poor Food List B
Ingredients: 1 quart Bing cherries with stems
　　　　　　　1 tbsp. pickling salt
　　　　　　　1 cup white vinegar
　　　　　　　1 cup water
Method: 1. Wash cherries leaving stems on; pack in sterile jars.
　　　　　2. Heat water, salt and vinegar until salt dissolves.
　　　　　3. Pour hot brine over cherries in jar to cover fruit.
　　　　　4. Seal and store at least 3 months before using.

PICKLED MUSHROOMS

Exchange 2 or 3 pickled mushrooms for: 1 Calorie Free Food List A
Ingredients: 2 quarts tiny button mushrooms
　　　　　　　4 cups white vinegar
　　　　　　　2 cups water
　　　　　　　2 tsps. pickling salt
　　　　　　　artificial liquid sweetener to taste
Method: 1. Wash mushrooms; do not peel.
　　　　　2. Cover with water; add salt; cook until tender; test with a toothpick; drain.
　　　　　3. Heat vinegar and 2 cups water; add sweetener to taste.
　　　　　4. Pack mushrooms in sterilized jars.
　　　　　5. Pour hot vinegar, water and sweetener over mushrooms to cover.
　　　　　6. Cover with sterile lids and seal; allow a few days to pickle before using.

APPLE CATSUP

Yield: Four ½ pint jars
Exchange 2 tsps. for: 1 Calorie Poor Food List B
Ingredients: 4 cups cooked apples, sieved
　　　　　　　1 tsp. ground cloves
　　　　　　　1 tsp. dry mustard
　　　　　　　1 tsp. cinnamon
　　　　　　　1 tbsp. salt
　　　　　　　2 onions
　　　　　　　2 cups vinegar
　　　　　　　2 tbsps. artificial liquid sweetener
Method: 1. Combine all ingredients except liquid sweetener; mix well.
　　　　　2. Bring to a boil; simmer one hour.
　　　　　3. Add liquid sweetener; while boiling hot, fill sterile jars.
　　　　　4. Seal tightly.

DILL PICKLES

Yield: 10 to 12 whole pickles

Exchange 1 pickle for: 1 Calorie Poor Food List B

Method: Use freshly picked cucumbers, 3 to 5 inches long; wash, soak overnight in cold water; drain thoroughly; place pieces of dill in bottom of clean sterilized jars; pack cucumbers into jars and place more dill on top.

> *Combine:* ½ cup table salt, or ¾ cup coarse salt, preferably not iodized
> 2 cups white vinegar
> 6 cups water

Bring to a boil and pour hot liquid over cucumbers; seal; let stand in a cool place at least 6 weeks before using.

ARTIFICIALLY SWEETENED GHERKINS OR MIXED PICKLES

Exchange 4 pieces pickle for: 1 Calorie Poor Food List B

Most favourite pickle recipes can be followed, omitting the sugar and adding artificial liquid sweetener to taste; always add the artificial liquid sweetener near end of cooking time.

UNCOOKED TOMATO PICKLE

Yield: 5 pints

Exchange: The caloric value of this pickle is so low that it may be eaten in moderation.

Ingredients: 4 quarts tomatoes
1½ cups chopped onion
½ cup salt
¼ cup sweet red pepper, chopped
4 cups diced celery
2½ cups cider vinegar
2 tbsps. mustard seed
artificial liquid sweetener to taste

Method: 1. Chop onion and tomatoes fine; place in separate containers.
2. Add ¼ cup salt to each and let stand 3 hours; mix tomato and onion; drain overnight.
3. Add remaining ingredients and pack in sterile jars.

CHILI SAUCE

Yield: about six ½ pint jars

Exchange: The caloric value of this pickle is so low that it may be eaten in moderation.

Ingredients: 18 tomatoes
2 green peppers
2 onions, medium
1 tbsp. salt
½ tsp. ground cloves
1 tsp. allspice
2 cups vinegar
3 tbsps. artificial liquid sweetener

Method: 1. Peel and chop tomatoes.
2. Chop peppers and onions fine.
3. Combine all ingredients **except** artificial liquid sweetener.
4. Simmer for 4 hours, or until thickened.
5. Add artificial liquid sweetener.
6. Pour boiling hot into sterile jars; seal.

Note: To make a brighter red sauce, use stick cinnamon, whole cloves, and whole allspice. Tie spices loosely in a piece of cheesecloth, and remove after cooking.

FRANKFURTER RELISH

Yield: about six ½ pint jars

Exchange 2 tsps. for: 1 Calorie Poor Food List B

Ingredients: 3½ sweet red peppers
3 lbs. green peppers
3 lbs. onions
4 cups vinegar
1 tsp. mustard seed
1 tbsp. dry mustard
1 tbsp. celery seed
2 tbsps. salt
1 tbsp. artificial liquid sweetener

Method: 1. Wash peppers, remove cores and seeds.
2. Peel onions; put onions and peppers through food chopper, using medium knife blade; cover with boiling water, and let stand 5 minutes.
3. Drain; add vinegar, spices, and salt.
4. Cook until vegetables are tender (about 15 minutes) stirring occasionally.
5. Add artificial liquid sweetener; pour boiling hot into sterile jars; seal.

REFERENCES

Exchange Lists for Meal Planning for Diabetics in Canada
— published by The Canadian Diabetic Association.

Manual for Diabetics in Canada
— published by The Canadian Diabetic Association.

Further information about these books and other literature can be obtained from:

THE CANADIAN DIABETIC ASSOCIATION
1491 Yonge Street
Toronto 7, Ontario

The National Diet Counselling Service of The Canadian Diabetic Association (1 Spadina Cres., Toronto 4, Ontario) and the Western Diet Counselling Service of the Association (10940 - 84th Street, Edmonton, Alberta) can provide exchange values per serving for many commercial products.

NOTES

NOTES

NOTES

NOTES

NOTES